BUCK ROGERS
IN THE 25TH CENTURY

BUCK ROGERS
IN THE 25TH CENTURY

WRITTEN BY JIM LAWRENCE
ILLUSTRATED BY GRAY MORROW

FOREWORD BY BUSTER CRABBE

quick fox

NEW YORK–LONDON

Printed in the United States of America.

International Standard Book Number: 0-8256-3221-8
Library of Congress Catalog Card Number: 81-50614

In Great Britain: Book Sales Ltd., 78 Newman Street, London W1P 3LA.

In Canada: Gage Trade Publishing, P.O. Box 5000, 164 Commander Blvd.,
          Agincourt, Ontario M1S 3C7.

Cover and Book Design: Tim Metevier
Assistant: Kari Ann Pagnano

FOREWORD

It was in the middle of the roaring twenties—1927 to be exact—when a newspaper syndicator named John Flint Dille determined that the world was ready for a science fiction space fantasy. Lindbergh had not yet flown the Atlantic; I had just won my first National Swimming Championship and was dreaming of the '28 Olympics in Amsterdam. Talking movies hadn't arrived, let alone Buck Rogers or interplanetary voyages, but Dille was certain that space travel—or at least a comic strip about it—was just around the corner. Dille had an editorial cartoonist from the *Detroit News* on his staff named Dick Calkins. All he needed was a writer. When Phillip Nowland brought in a short story he had just published called "Armageddon-2419 A.D.," Dille knew he had a match. The hero of the story was Anthony "Buck" Rogers.

Buck and Wilma cling with magnetic grapplers to a derelict spaceship (1931). © 1981 Robert C. Dille

Calkins' first sketches had Buck surrounded by prehistoric animals, such as dinosaurs and brontosaurs, but Dille quickly changed that. In his second attempt, Calkins

created Buck's girlfriend, Wilma Deering, Dr. Huer, and the diabolical "Killer" Kane—all the characters who would capture the imagination of the country.

Kayla and Killer Kane plot while Buck, near death, floats in space (1931).
© 1981 Robert C. Dille

The first strip, "Buck Rogers 2429 A.D." appeared on January 7, 1929. In it, Buck, a World War I veteran, had a job surveying "an abandoned mine near Pittsburgh in which the atmosphere had a peculiar, pungent tang and the crumbling rock glowed strangely." Overcome by gas, Buck collapsed but didn't die. He awoke 500 years later, a modern Rip Van Winkle in a world full of force rays, robot armies, gravity repeller rays, mechanical moles, and teleradioscopes.

Soon the strip, now titled "Buck Rogers in the 25th Century," was appearing in as many as 450 newspapers and seventeen languages. It was so successful it spawned another now-famous strip, Flash Gordon, and countless radio shows, books, movies, and premiums, which captivated the nation and paved the way for future generations of Trekkies and Star Wars fans.

The comic strip was a near institution in the thirties and forties. My friend Ray Bradbury recalls that time: "The door burst open. A boy, myself, leapt out, eyes blazing, mouth gasping for breath, hands seizing at the paper to grapple it wide so that the hungry soul of one of Waukegan, Illinois' finest small intellects could feed upon Buck Rogers."

The comic strip continued on through the fifties; in 1967, for a variety of reasons, it was discontinued. But the interest and demand went on. Twelve years later, at the instigation of Bob Dille, grandson of Buck's creator, John Dille, and through the efforts of *New York Times* syndicate illustrator Gray Morrow and writer Jim Lawrence, Buck reappeared in comic strips. The strip was snapped up eagerly and now appears in many languages throughout the world.

My first involvement with Buck Rogers was in 1939, while I was with Universal Studios. Even though Buck was the first science fiction comic strip, it wasn't the first movie. I had already done two Flash Gordon serials when the studio asked me to do Buck Rogers. In both cases, the scripts for the serial were based on the comic strip. One change from the strip that I recall was being freeze-dried rather than overcome by gas.

WHILE WILMA, ON DIONE, STRUGGLED TO REGAIN HER LOST MEMORY — AND HUER FUMED AT HIS INABILITY TO LOCATE US, THE **MYSTERY SHIP** CIRCLED MANY TIMES AROUND THE PLANET JUPITER TO CHECK ITS TERRIFIC MOMENTUM—

COPYRIGHT JOHN F. DILLE CO.
REG. U S PAT. OFF.

AND FINALLY— ON RETARDING ROCKET BLAST— PLUNGED DOWN INTO THE JOVIAN ATMOSPHERE.

Predictions by Richard Calkins (above left to right): orbiting spaceship; retro-rocket (1932). © 1981 Robert C. Dille

It took about six weeks to finish thirteen episodes of Buck Rogers, and I was paid the princely sum of $500 by Paramount, while I was on loan from Universal. We never did do a second serial of Buck, possibly because Flash was out first and was more successful, but both of them were enjoyable to do. I was really pleased to see Buck Rogers revived in a television series. Gil Girard is a charming and worthy successor as Buck. In one of the

episodes I was the "old gunslinger" flying in the rocket next to Gil's; it was great fun to compare the old serials with the TV series.

Harpo Marx-like observers await a momentous decision in this vintage clip from the 1939 Paramount Studios Buck Rogers serial.

Ray Bradbury remembers giving away his Buck Rogers collection: "My Buck Rogers collection! Which was like giving away my head, my heart, my soul, and half a lung. I walked wounded for a year after that. I grieved and cursed myself for having so dumbly tossed aside what was, in essence, the greatest love of my life." Having played Buck Rogers first, it's a great experience to see him come back to life on TV and in these pages. There was a thrill with Buck, and it comes through in the book. It's like getting back what you thought you'd already given away.

Buster Crabbe

2

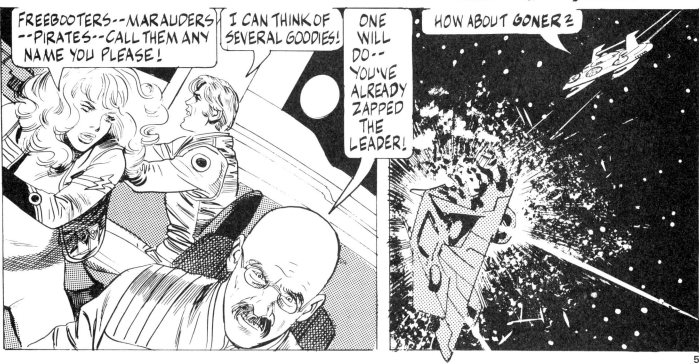

AN EERIE SPECTACLE CONFRONTS THE EARTHLINGS AS THEIR SHIP HURTLES THROUGH THE VOID!

THE SARGASSO VORTEX! SPACEMEN HAVE YARNED ABOUT IT SINCE TIME-WARP FLIGHT BEGAN!

AND NOW WE KNOW HOW THOSE HULKS GOT TRAPPED! THEY WERE SUCKED IN BY THE SAME FORCE THAT'S GRIPPING US!

ANY CLUE FROM THE INSTRUMENT GYRATIONS, DOC?

EVERY PARTICLE IN THAT MORASS IS MAGNETICALLY CHARGED! SOMEHOW IT'S ALL BEEN CONCENTRATED INTO A POWERFUL ATTRACTOR BEAM!

WITH A SUDDEN JOLT-- STARLAB CRASHES INTO THE DREAD SARGASSO VORTEX TO JOIN THE OTHER GHOSTLY SPACE HULKS, TRAPPED THERE LIKE FLIES IN A WEB!

CAN'T WE REV UP ENOUGH POWER TO PULL LOOSE?

'FRAID NOT, WILMA! THE MAGNETIC PULL OF THE VORTEX SEEMS TO BE STALLING OUR ION ENGINE!

HOLD IT, GANG! WE CAME HERE LOOKING FOR A SHIP CALLED CYGNET-- LET'S SEE IF SHE'S OUT THERE!

THERE IT IS! CYGNET-- THE SHIP WE CAME TO FIND!

STARLAB'S SEARCH BEAM PLAYS OVER THE HULKS OF ANCIENT SPACECRAFT TRAPPED IN THE SARGASSO VORTEX--

NO WONDER SHE NEVER RETURNED TO EARTH BASE!

GOOD LORD! IS IT POSSIBLE ANY OF THE CREW COULD STILL BE ALIVE-- AFTER BEING MAROONED HERE FOR FIFTY YEARS?!

SOMEBODY TRANSMITTED THEIR CODE CALL! LET'S GET SUITED UP AND FIND OUT WHO-- OR WHAT!

OKAY, YORYX-- IF YOU'RE BOSS OF THIS GALACTIC JUNKYARD, MAYBE YOU CAN TELL US WHAT HAPPENED TO CYGNET AND HER CREW!

MY ATTRACTOR BEAM DREW HER HERE INTO MY WEB-- AS IT DREW YOUR SHIP, CAPTAIN!

DOUBTLESS YOU'VE ALREADY ENCOUNTERED MY PIRATE ALLIES? .... IN EARTHLING TERMS, THEY SERVE AS MY JACKALS -- MY SCAVENGERS!

ONCE A SPACECRAFT IS DISABLED, THEY SIEZE ITS CARGO-- BUT ITS CREW ARE MINE!!

LAWRENCE & MORROW 10-11

WAIT! NOW I KNOW WHO YOU ARE!!

I'M ASTONISHED, COLONEL DEERING! I DIDN'T REALIZE ANY EARTHLING KNEW OF MY EXISTENCE---

CORRECTION! I MAY NOT KNOW WHO YOU ARE -- BUT I CAN GUESS WHAT YOU ARE!

UNLIKE YOUR PIRATE STOOGES, YOU'RE AFTER LIVING PREY! SOMETHING TELLS ME YOU'RE A SURVIVOR OF THAT GHASTLY RACE OF SPACE VAMPIRES!

LAWRENCE & MORROW 10-12

SPACE VAMPIRES! ARE YOU KIDDING, WILMA?

NO WAY! WHEN THEIR OWN PLANET DIED, THEY TOOK TO PROWLING THE GALAXY TO SUCK THE LIFE FORCE FROM OTHER BEINGS!

HOLD IT! WHAT'S THIS JIVE ABOUT SPACE VAMPIRES SUCKING LIFE FORCES?

IN YOGA, IT'S CALLED PRANA! IN THE MARTIAL ARTS THEY CALLED IT KI -- IN YOUR OWN TIME I MEAN, BUCK!

© 1979 Robert C. Dille Dist. by NYT Special Features

YORYX'S RACE AQUIRED THE ABILITY TO DRAIN THE LIFE FORCE DIRECTLY FROM OTHER BEINGS--LIKE RADIATION FROM AN ANTENNA!

LAWRENCE & MORROW 10-13

THAT'S WHY HIS RACE WAS HUNTED DOWN BY GALACTIC PATROLS -- AND DESTROYED!

EXCEPT FOR MYSELF, COLONEL DEERING! HERE IN MY LAIR IN THE SARGASSO VORTEX, I SURVIVED!

20

BUCK ROGERS ®
IN THE 25TH CENTURY

AS YORYX SHOWS OFF THE CONTROLS BY WHICH HE TRAPS PASSING SPACECRAFT IN THE SARGASSO VORTEX-- BUCK SEIZES HIS CHANCE!

THE SPACE VAMPIRE REACTS WITH TERRIFYING **STRENGTH** AND **FEROCITY** BEFORE BUCK CAN TAKE HIM BY SURPRISE!

SMOKIN' ROCKETS! THIS DUDE'S **INHUMAN!**-- AS IF THAT'S ANY NEWS!!

WILMA!...**WILMA!** SNAP OUT OF IT!!

WITH YORYX'S HYPNOTIC INFLUENCE WEAKENED BY HIS STRUGGLE WITH BUCK-- WILMA GRADUALLY RESPONDS TO HER PARTNER'S CALL!

BUCK--!

"HE NEEDS ME!"

LAWRENCE + MORROW 10-28

MAYBE THIS WILL HELP--!!

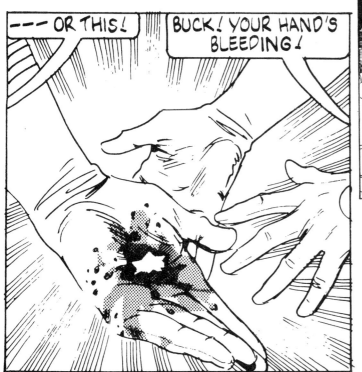

24

SO MARK ORBEN'S BEEN FOUND ALIVE!

YES -- IN MUTANT ZONE 5! IT'S ORBEN, ALL RIGHT! WE'VE HAD ABSOLUTE VIDEO-COMPUTER IDENTIFICATION!

HMM... WELL, WHAT'S HIS STORY? ANY EXPLANATION OF WHERE HE'S BEEN THESE PAST FEW MONTHS?

ORBEN MARK, 49
CLICK!

NONE! HE'S UTTERLY DISORIENTED -- CAN'T EVEN COMMUNICATE INTELLIGIBLY!

SO OBVIOUSLY THERE'S NO WAY OF TELLING WHAT HAPPENED TO HIM!

YOU REALIZE, DR. HUER -- MARK ORBEN'S MEMORY BANK -- ER, BRAIN -- WAS CRAMMED WITH TOP-SECRET DATA ON STAR-COM'S NEWEST SPACECRAFT!

LAWRENCE + MORROW 11-9

QUITE! WHICH RAISES THE POSSIBILITY THAT SOME ALIEN ENEMY AGENT MAY HAVE FORCIBLY DEBRIEFED HIM!

EXACTLY! THEY COULD HAVE PICKED HIS BRAINS -- BY PSYCHO-CHEMICAL OR ELECTRO-HYPNOTIC MEANS!

WELL, WILMA -- I THINK SECURITY REQUIRES THAT ORBEN BE BROUGHT HERE BY SOMEONE OF NO LESS THAN COLONEL RANK!

CREAM AND SUGAR, SIR?

ER -- STRAIGHT! I MEAN... BLACK!

WITH A CAPTAIN FOR BACK-UP?

WHAT'S THIS MUTANT ZONE WE'RE HEADED FOR, WILMA?

THESE ZONES RESULTED FROM THE HOLOCAUST WARS OF THE 21ST AND 22ND CENTURIES, BUCK --

-- WHEN MANKIND BLIGHTED MOTHER EARTH WITH THE DEADLY FALLOUT FROM NUCLEO-LASER WEAPONRY AND BIO-CHEMICAL TOXINS!

WHOLE AREAS WERE DEVASTATED?

FOR A TIME, YES! THEN AS VARIOUS LIFE FORMS BEGAN TO BREED AGAIN, MUTATIONS APPEARED --

-- SOME OF THEM STRANGE AND RATHER TERRIBLE!

LAWRENCE + MORROW 11-10

BUCK ROGERS IN THE 25TH CENTURY

THE MYSTERY OF THE MIND-BLOWN STARSHIP-DESIGNER DEEPENS ...!

YOU'VE NO IDEA WHO FIRED THOSE RAY-GUN BLASTS AT ORBEN?

BUCK CHASED THE CREATURE -- FROM HIS DESCRIPTION, I'D SAY IT WAS A **HAIRY MUTANT!**

WILMA'S TRYING TO **DECODE** MARK ORBEN'S GIBBERISH SOUNDS -- BY MAKING HIS **MENTAL IMAGES** VISIBLE ON A COMMUNICATIONS TRANSDUCER!

I STILL THINK HE'S SPEAKING SOME KIND OF **MUTANT JARGON!** ... CAN YOU MAKE ANYTHING OF HIS BRAIN-WAVE TRANSMISSIONS, DR. HUER?

HMM, I SEE ... WELL, OUR IMMEDIATE PROBLEM IS TO FIGURE OUT WHAT ORBEN'S TRYING TO TELL US!

YES, THE IMAGES ARE COMING THROUGH CLEARLY ENOUGH!

I'VE A HUNCH THOSE BUILDINGS MAY BE THE **GOOD HOPE HOSPITAL** IN THE *MUTANT JUNGLES* OF CENTRAL EUROPE ...

".. IN WHICH CASE, THE WOMAN COULD BE **DR. TALYA THANE** -- WHO RUNS IT!

BUT WHY THAT HAIRY MUTANT BUCK SAW SHOULD WANT TO **KILL** ORBEN -- IS FRANKLY MORE THAN I CAN GUESS!

WILMA'S TRANSMITTING ORBEN'S **BRAIN-WAVE IMAGES** BACK TO DR. HUER -- WHO HAS SUDDENLY CLUED-IN TO WHAT ORBEN'S JABBERING ABOUT!

GJ≥RGЧ ⊐Ε CJ𝄆Л⊏𝄆𝄆!

THIS **GOOD HOPE HOSPITAL** -- WHAT EXACTLY IS IT, DOCTOR?

A PIONEERING MEDICAL MISSION, WILMA -- TO SOME OF THE WILDER TRIBES OF THE **MUTANT JUNGLE!**

HOW'D YOU RECOGNIZE THE SET-UP, DOC -- HAVE YOU SEEN IT?

ONLY PICTURES, ACTUALLY -- THE WOMAN WHO RUNS THE MISSION, **DR. TALYA THANE,** DOESN'T ENCOURAGE VISITORS!

BUCK'S GOT A POINT -- SHE DOES LOOK SURPRISINGLY YOUNG AND CHIC FOR THE HEAD OF A JUNGLE MEDICAL MISSION!

IF YOUR GUESS IS RIGHT ABOUT THIS DAME BEING DR. THANE -- SHE SURE DOESN'T FIT THE USUAL MISSIONARY IMAGE, DOC!

I'D HAVE EXPECTED SOMEONE OLDER MYSELF, WILMA!

TALYA THANE'S NOT ONLY EARNED A NAME IN RESEARCH -- SHE'S BEEN RUNNING GOOD HOPE HOSPITAL FOR YEARS! BUT SHE SHUNS ALL PUBLICITY -- EVEN THE DESCRIPTIONS I'VE READ OF HER SEEM TO VARY!

OKAY -- SO WE ALL AGREE -- THIS THANE FEMALE'S QUITE A **DISH** TO BE RUNNING A JUNGLE MEDICAL MISSION! THE BIG QUESTION REMAINS ---

⊂Λ·∿) ⊐ϤϤ (Ϥ⊐-⊥≅ Ρ:∿!

WHAT'S SHE GOT TO DO WITH THIS GUY, MARK ORBEN -- WHO DISAPPEARS, THEN TURNS UP JABBERING MUTANT JARGON?

THE OBVIOUS ANSWER TO THAT, BUCK MY BOY -- IS FOR YOU AND WILMA TO GO SEE DR. THANE AND FIND OUT!

BUCK ROGERS IN THE 25th CENTURY

AT THE GOOD HOPE HOSPITAL -- BUCK AND WILMA ARE GREETED BY ARMED GUARDS -- AND A SCANNER GUN!

NATURALLY SHE'S INTERESTED IN ALL VISITORS!

I TAKE IT YOUR BOSS-LADY'S GIVING US THE ONCE-OVER WITH THAT CAMERA-EYE!

IN SOME MORE THAN OTHERS, IT SEEMS -- JUDGING FROM THE WAY YOUR SCANNER KEEPS LINGERING ON CAPTAIN ROGERS!

HAD I KNOWN I WAS TO BE SO HONORED -- YOU MAY BE SURE I WOULD HAVE **PREPARED** FOR YOUR VISIT!

NO DOUBT!

LAWRENCE + MORROW 11-25

I'M SO GLAD YOU FINALLY CONDESCENDED TO MEET US, DR. THANE!

© 1979 Robert C. Dille. Dist. by NYT Special Feature

LURG! WILL YOU PLEASE SEE TO REFRESHMENTS -- FOR THESE DISTINGUISHED REPRESENTATIVES OF THE EARTH FEDERATION!

LURG?

A **MUTANT**, OF COURSE -- BUT MORE INTELLIGENT THAN MOST! HE'S SERVED ME FAITHFULLY FOR MANY YEARS!

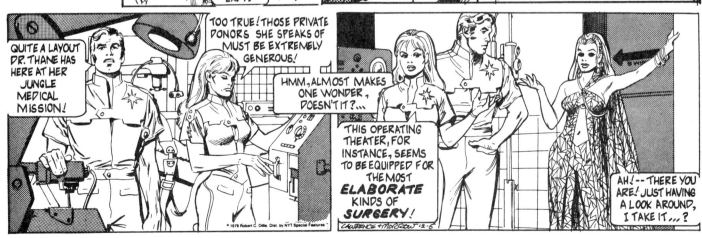

41

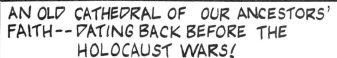

42

BUCK ROGERS IN THE 25TH CENTURY

MUST YOU WASTE SO MUCH TIME QUESTIONING THAT COMPUTER?

SURELY YOU'RE NOT STILL CONCERNED OVER WHAT COLONEL DEERING MAY HAVE THOUGHT -- ABOUT FINDING US TOGETHER?

ANGRY AT SEEING BUCK APPARENTLY FALL FOR THE FEMININE WILES OF DR. TALYA THANE-- WILMA HAS COME BY HERSELF TO PERSUE A LEAD IN THE ORBEN MYSTERY!

...BUT SUDDENLY SHE'S NO LONGER ALONE!

LURG! SO IT WAS YOUR MISTRESS WHO SENT ME THAT MESSAGE --!

-- JUST TO TRICK ME INTO COMING HERE!

URRHH! YOU SHOULD NOT HAVE INTERFERED IN THE DOCTOR LADY'S AFFAIRS!

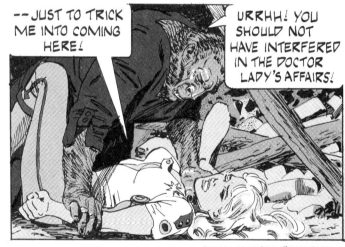

MEANWHILE--

YOU'RE RIGHT, DOCTOR! LOOKS LIKE A WASTE OF TIME CROSS-CHECKING ORBEN'S NAME IN YOUR HOSPITAL DATA BANK!

BUT OUR TIME TOGETHER NEEDN'T BE WASTED!

WHUP! - HERE'S AN OVERRIDE ON TRANSMISSION- ONE OF YOUR GUARDS...

TRANSMISSION FOR CAPTAIN ROGERS --FROM EARTH FEDERATION HQ!

LAWRENCE & MORROW 12-16

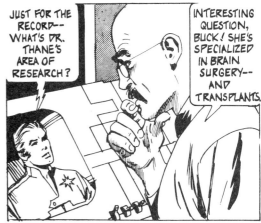

BUCK ROGERS IN THE 25TH CENTURY

URRH... IT IS GOOD THE DR. LADY WANTS YOU SAVED! NOW LURG WILL NOT HAVE TO **KILL** SUCH A BEAUTY!

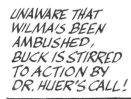

UNAWARE THAT WILMA'S BEEN AMBUSHED, BUCK IS STIRRED TO ACTION BY DR. HUER'S CALL!

IT'S GOTTA BE MORE THAN CHANCE, DOC— ALL THOSE OLD FOLKS DISAPPEARING IN THE MUTANT JUNGLE....

I'D BETTER TELL WILMA!

WHERE'S COLONEL DEERING—THE OFFICER WHO WAS WITH ME— HAVE YOU SEEN HER?

N-NO! PAVIL KNOWS NOTHING AND SEES NOTHING!

DON'T GIVE ME THAT! YOU'VE BEEN WORKING AROUND HERE ALL AFTERNOON— YOU **MUST** 'VE SEEN HER! WHAT'RE YOU AFRAID OF? C'MON— TALK!

LAURENCE MORROW 12-23

1979 Robert C. Dille. Dist. by NYT Special Features

P-PLEASE! LET ME GO! I WILL ANSWER IF YOU PROMISE NOT TO T-TELL DR. THANE! THE LADY OFFICER YOU ARE SEEKING WENT OFF WITH THE OLD SHE-MUTANT CALLED ZENYL...

MEANWHILE~~~ UHR! LURG HAS DONE AS YOU COMMANDED, MY LADY!

GOOD! TAKE HER TO THE OPERATING ROOM!

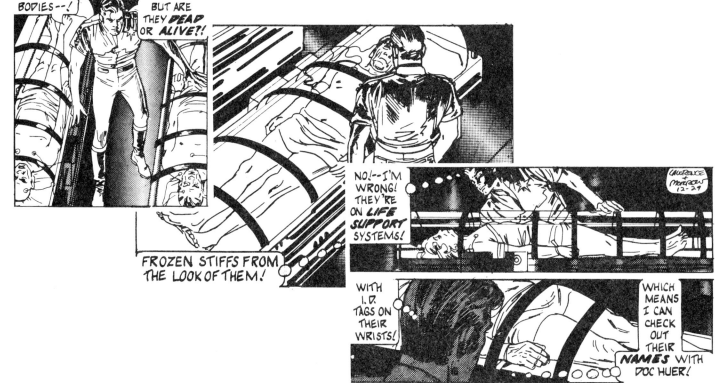

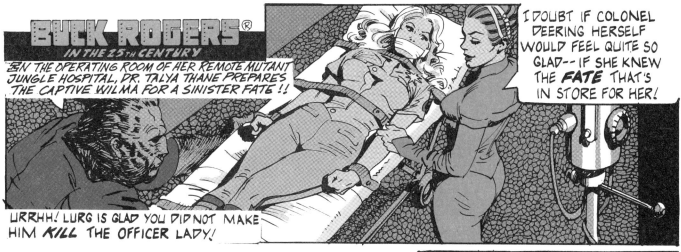

BUCK ROGERS IN THE 25TH CENTURY

IN THE OPERATING ROOM OF HER REMOTE MUTANT JUNGLE HOSPITAL, DR. TALYA THANE PREPARES THE CAPTIVE WILMA FOR A SINISTER FATE!!

I DOUBT IF COLONEL DEERING HERSELF WOULD FEEL QUITE SO GLAD-- IF SHE KNEW THE *FATE* THAT'S IN STORE FOR HER!

URRHH! LURG IS GLAD YOU DID NOT MAKE HIM *KILL* THE OFFICER LADY!

ZENYL'S STORY ABOUT DECOYING WILMA INTO THE JUNGLE HAS LED BUCK TO AN ANGRY HUNT FOR DR. THANE-- AND A *GRISLY FIND* IN HER LAB!

IF THEIR ID TAGS BEAR OUT MY HUNCH-- THIS COULD BE WHERE THE BEAUTIFUL TALYA MADE HER FIRST *BIG MISTAKE!*

AFTER RADIOING DR. HUER ---

YOU'RE RIGHT, BUCK! THOSE ARE THE NAMES OF THE LAST THREE ELDERLY PERSONS REPORTED MISSING IN THE MUTANT JUNGLE!

AND YOU SAY TALYA THANE'S SPECIALTIES ARE BRAIN SURGERY AND TRANSPLANTS!

THAT'S CORRECT! SO--?

STOP ME IF THE SAME THOUGHTS ALREADY HIT YOU, DOC -- BUT DOESN'T THAT SUGGEST WHY SHE'S GOT THOSE THREE OLDSTERS ON LIFE SUPPORT SYSTEMS?

© 1979 Robert C. Dille Dist. by NYT Special Features

LAWRENCE & MORROW 12-30

AT THAT MOMENT---

WHAT NOW, MY LADY?

FETCH ZENYL-- THEN PREPARE YOURSELF TO TAKE PART IN THE OPERATION!

DR. HUER CONFIRMS BUCK'S HUNCH--THAT THE NAME-TAGGED FIGURES IN TALYA'S LAB WERE THREE OF THE OLDSTERS WHO 'DISAPPEARED' IN THE MUTANT JUNGLE!

WHAT EXACTLY ARE YOU SUGGESTING, BUCK?

THOSE MISSING OLDIES WERE ALL *RICH*--RIGHT? OKAY, SO IF TALYA THANE'S SPECIALIZES IN *BRAIN SURGERY* AND *TRANSPLANTS* ---

-- MAYBE THEY CAME TO HER TO BUY THEMSELVES *NEW* YOUNGER BODIES!

YOU'RE IMPLYING THOSE WEALTHY OLD INVALIDS WENT TO TALYA THANE'S CLINIC TO HAVE THEIR BRAINS TRANSPLANTED ---

--INTO BRAND-NEW HEALTHY BODIES! SURE!

WHY ELSE WOULD SHE HAVE THEM HERE ON LIFE-SUPPORT SYSTEMS--UNLESS THEY'RE WAITING FOR A TRANSPLANT?

WHERE WOULD SHE GET THE NECESSARY *BODIES?*

IN A PLACE LIKE THE GOOD HOPE HOSPITAL? ARE YOU KIDDING, DOC?

BUT GOOD HEAVENS, BUCK! WHAT YOU'RE SUGGESTING WOULDN'T INVOLVE MERE *ORGAN* DONORS--!

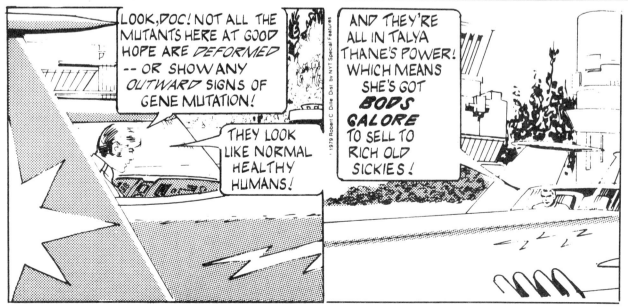

LOOK, DOC! NOT ALL THE MUTANTS HERE AT GOOD HOPE ARE *DEFORMED* -- OR SHOW ANY *OUTWARD* SIGNS OF GENE MUTATION!

THEY LOOK LIKE NORMAL HEALTHY HUMANS!

AND THEY'RE ALL IN TALYA THANE'S POWER! WHICH MEANS SHE'S GOT *BODS GALORE* TO SELL TO RICH OLD SICKIES!

BUCK ROGERS®
IN THE 25TH CENTURY

REMOVE COLONEL DEERINGS GAG!

--- SO WE CAN BE SURE SHE *APPRECIATES* THE BRILLIANT *SURGICAL* FEAT WE ARE ABOUT TO PERFORM ON HER!

WILMA BLANCHES IN HORROR AS SHE REALIZES HER *BRAIN* IS ABOUT TO BE TRANSPLANTED INTO A *HAG'S BODY!*

LAWRENCE + MORROW 1-6

SO THAT'S WHY SOMEONE OLD-- LIKE MARK ORBEN-- WOULD COME HERE AND *DISAPPEAR!*

OF COURSE! TO BE *REBORN* IN MORE YOUTHFUL FORM!

© 1979 Robert C. Dille Dist. by NYT Special Features

IN FACT YOU'RE *LIVING EVIDENCE* THAT YOUTH CAN BE RESTORED-- RIGHT, DR. THANE?

BUCK--!

SOMETHING TELLS ME IF YOU HADN'T STOLEN POOR ZENYL'S BODY-- *YOU'D* BE THAT OLD CRONE WHO'S NOW LYING ON THE OPERATING TABLE!

BUT WE'LL GO INTO THAT LATER! *UNSTRAP* COLONEL DEERING, LURG!

INSTEAD-- THE HAIRY MUTANT SUDDENLY STRAIGHTENS UP-- AND HURLS A CYLINDER OF ANESTHETIC GAS---!

BUCK! LOOK OUT--!

YOU ASKED FOR IT, DOC! NOW KEEP AWAY FROM THAT SCALPEL!

ONE OF YOU MUTANTS UNSTRAP THE LADY OFFICER!

OKAY, DOC-- GET ON THE VIDEO-COM AND TELL YOUR GUARDS *NOT* TO INTERFERE WITH OUR TAKE-OFF!

SORRY CAPTAIN! YOU AND THE COLONEL WILL NEVER LEAVE HERE *ALIVE!*

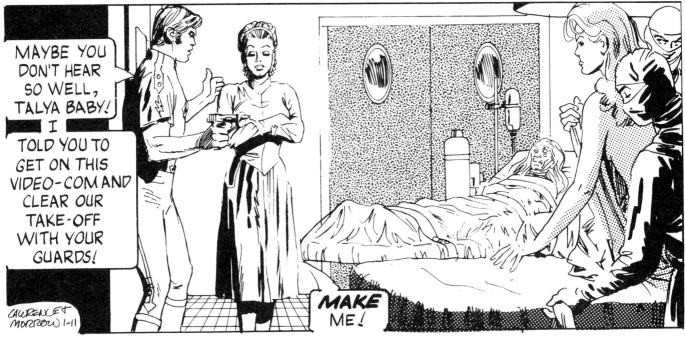

MAYBE YOU DON'T HEAR SO WELL, TALYA BABY! I TOLD YOU TO GET ON THIS VIDEO-COM AND CLEAR OUR TAKE-OFF WITH YOUR GUARDS!

MAKE ME!

IT'LL BE A PLEASURE--!

GO ON! YOU HEARD WHAT THE CAPTAIN SAID! OR WOULD YOU RATHER I DO SOME PLASTIC SURGERY ON YOU--WITHOUT ANESTHESIA?!

YOU CALLED, MY LADY?

COLONEL DEERING AND CAPTAIN ROGERS ARE ABOUT TO TAKE OFF! UNDER *NO* CIRCUMSTANCES WILL YOU INTERFERE WITH THEIR DEPARTURE!

AND BRING ALONG ZENYL ...UNDERSTAND?

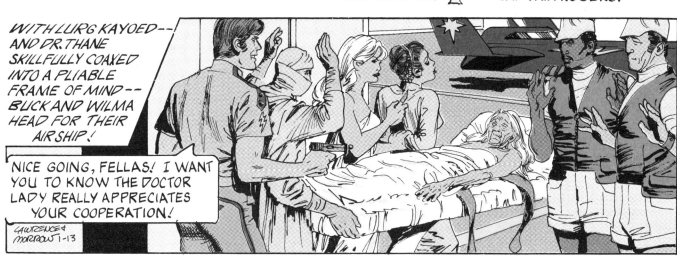

IT'S REALLY KIND OF YOU, DOCTOR, TO HELP US GET *SAFELY AIRBORNE* THIS WAY!

DR. THANE HAS ORDERED HER GUARDS *NOT TO INTERFERE* AS BUCK AND WILMA PREPARE TO TAKE OFF---

...BUT THEN YOU WOULDN'T WANT THIS *SCALPEL* TO SLIP IN MY HAND-- WOULD YOU, DEAR?

LATER... IS ZENYL AWAKE FROM THE ANESTHETIC?

NOT YET...BUT SHE'LL BE CONCIOUS WHEN WE REACH CHICAGO-- IN PLENTY OF TIME TO TESTIFY AGAINST THE 'DOCTOR LADY'!

WHAT D'YOU THINK THEY'LL SAY ABOUT YOU BEING OUT OF UNIFORM, MON COLONEL?

YOU SAY ANYMORE AND YOU'LL BE *OUT OF THE SHIP* WALKING HOME, MON CAPITAINE!!

YESSIR, MA'AM SIR, YOUR COLONEL SHIP, SIR!

...UPON LANDING

DON'T ASK!

I WOULDN'T ASK....?!

IN NEW CHICAGO, THE FULL MACABRE STORY OF DR. THANE AND HER JUNGLE CLINIC IS NOW KNOWN---

YOU'VE MADE QUITE A RACKET, DOCTOR, OUT OF TRANSPLANTING ELDERLY PATIENTS' BRAINS INTO YOUNGER BODIES!

ONE CLIENT WAS MARK ORBEN-- WHOSE BODY YOU SWITCHED FOR THAT OF A YOUNG MUTANT!

YOU YOURSELF TOOK THE FORM OF THIS ONCE BEAUTIFUL GIRL, ZENYL!

WHAT'LL HAPPEN TO TALYA, DOC?

DETENTION AREA

A *VERY IMPARTIAL* JUDGE WILL DECIDE THAT, BUCK!

YOU HAVE BEEN FOUND GUILTY OF A *HEINOUS* CRIME, DOCTOR--

--DEALING IN HUMAN BODIES FOR PROFIT!

-- AND CONDEMNING YOUTHFUL VICTIMS TO THE HORROR OF *IMPRISONMENT* IN AGED FORMS!

NOW YOUR OWN BRAIN WILL BE RETURNED TO THE SKULL OF THAT *WRINKLED CRONE* WHO IS *REALLY YOU!*

SHE MAY BE RUTHLESS-- BUT SHE'S STILL A-BRILLIANT SURGEON!

AS THE BRAIN OF THE 'BEAUTIFUL' DR. TALYA THANE IS TRANSPLANTED BACK INTO ITS ORIGINAL AGED BODY---

REST ASSURED, HER MEDICAL SKILL WILL BE PUT TO GOOD USE--UNDER PROPER SUPERVISION, OF COURSE!

1979 Robert C. Dille. Dist. by N.Y.T. Special Features

CAN YOU COME TO STAR-COM AT ONCE, DR. HUER? I'M AFRAID THE VOSTRIAN CRISIS IS HEATING UP AGAIN!

YOU KNOW HOW VITAL SYNTHON IS IN PRODUCING EARTH'S FOOD AND FUEL SUPPLY, DOCTOR--

YES, YES! AND THE PLANET VOSTRIA'S OUR ONLY SOURCE!

1979 Robert C. Dille. Dist. by N.Y.T. Special Features

I'M FULLY AWARE OF ALL THAT-- AND THE FACT THAT VOSTRIA'S IN A STATE OF ARMED TURMOIL!

WHAT'S MORE, I GATHER WE EARTHLINGS ARE NOT TOO POPULAR THERE AT THE MOMENT!

SO WHAT ELSE IS NEW?

AN ARMED CONFRONTATION BETWEEN A VOSTRIAN PATROL CRUISER AND ONE OF OUR TRANSPORTS -- THAT COULD LEAD TO WAR!

MEANWHILE--

WHAT EXACTLY IS HAPPENING ON VOSTRIA?

AN EARTH SHIP LOADED WITH SYNTHON HAS BEEN STOPPED FROM LEAVING THE PLANET!

THE BRAIN TRANSPLANT OPERATION IS OVER ... DR. THANE'S BACK IN HER OLD BODY -- AND ZENYL'S NOW HER BEAUTIFUL YOUNG SELF AGAIN!

YOU NEEDN'T GO BACK TO THE MUTANT JUNGLE, ZENYL!

BUT I WANT TO! YOU SEE, I'VE A--A SWEETHEART WAITING FOR ME! AND NOW HE'LL RECOGNIZE ME AGAIN!

OUR STARSHIP, CONSTITUTION, HAS REACHED THE PLANET VOSTRIA---

AS TERRAN ENVOY, I REQUEST AN AUDIENCE WITH YOUR NEW RULER!

THE REGENT RAISULI HAS GRACIOUSLY CONSENTED TO HEAR YOUR PLEA THAT WE GO ON SUPPLYING EARTH WITH SYNTHON!

BEFORE WE DISCUSS TRADE TERMS, YOUR EXCELLENCY--OUR TRANSPORT AND ITS CREW MUST FIRST BE RELEASED!

FOOL! IF EARTH THINKS IT CAN STILL DICTATE TO VOSTRIA--YOU ARE IN FOR A MOST UNPLEASANT SURPRISE!

YOU MAY TAKE BACK MY TERMS, EARTHLING! YOUR TRANSPORT CREW WILL BE TRIED AS SPIES!

I SHALL THEN INFORM YOUR MASTERS OF OUR FUTURE PRICE FOR SYNTHON!

THE TERRAN ENVOY RETURNS TO THE STARSHIP, CONSTITUTION, TO REPORT THE FAILURE OF HIS MISSION---

CONSTITUTION 5

ANY NEWS YET?

BAD--JUDGING FROM HIS CODE FLASH! WHICH MEANS THE NEXT STEP MAY BE UP TO US, BUCK!

A "TRIAL" WILL BE HELD OF THE CAPTURED TRANSPORT CREW!

ON WHAT GROUNDS?

THE REGENT RAISULI HIMSELF HAS CONDESCENDED TO COME AND INFORM YOU OF YOUR FATE!

DO YOU NEED TO BE TOLD OF YOUR OWN THIEVERY AND ESPIONAGE?

MEANWHILE---

YOU READ MY CODE FLASH, NO DOUBT?

THEIR NUTTY DICTATOR AIMS TO STONEWALL IT, RIGHT?

UNLESS WE CAN CHANGE HIS SO-CALLED MIND!

BUCK ROGERS IN THE 25TH CENTURY

AN EARTH TRANSPORT HAS BEEN SEIZED-- AND ITS CREW ARE BEING HELD HOSTAGE ON THE PLANET VOSTRIA!

YOUR PATROL CRUISER TOOK OUR CARGO -- THEY SAID THAT'S ALL THEY WANTED! WHY ARE YOU HOLDING *US*?!

SILENCE, DOG! YOU TERRANS HAVE PLUNDERED OUR PLANET OF ITS PRICELESS SYNTHON LONG ENOUGH!

EARTH'S ENVOY TO VOSTRIA HAS RETURNED TO HIS STARSHIP TO REPORT ON THE CAPTURED TRANSPORT...

© 1979 Robert C. Dille. Dist. by NYT Special Features

THE NEW REGENT'S NOT ONLY CUTTING OFF OUR SUPPLY OF SYNTHON -- HE MEANS TO MAKE *EXAMPLES* OF THE TRANSPORT CREW!

BY HOLDING SOME KIND OF PHONY *SHOW TRIAL*, NO DOUBT!

EXACTLY! HE MAY EVEN HAVE THEM CONDEMNED AND EXECUTED -- AS 'SPIES' OR 'PIRATES'!

YOU MEAN *IF* HE CAN HANG ONTO THEM THAT LONG!

LATER-- A SMALL SCOUTCRAFT SLIPS AWAY FROM THE ORBITING STARSHIP...

YOU HEARD WHAT THE ENVOY SAID, BUCK ... WHATEVER WE INTEND TO DO WILL HAVE TO BE ON OUR OWN!

WHO'S ARGUING, COLONEL?

WHILE ON THE NIGHT SIDE OF VOSTRIA---

ARE YOU CERTAIN OF THIS, JANKOR?

THE DETECTOR DOES NOT LIE! THE INTRUDER CRAFT IS DEFINITELY HEADING THIS WAY!

THE ENVOY'S MISSION TO VOSTRIA *HAS* FAILED! SO NOW--

YOU HAVE A PLAN, COLONEL, FOR THIS LITTLE COMMANDO JOB?

OUR FIRST CONCERN HAS TO BE LANDING SAFELY--AND UNDETECTED, BUCK!

IF WE SURVIVE THAT-- WE'LL SCOUT THE SPACEPORT AND FIND OUT WHERE THE HOSTAGES ARE BEING HELD!

LET'S NOT QUIBBLE, PLEASE-- I NEVER DID LIKE *IFFY* ANSWERS!

WAS IT REALLY WISE, COMMODORE --LETTING COLONEL DEERING AND CAPTAIN ROGERS EMBARK ON SUCH A RISKY MISSION?

I'D NO CHOICE, ENVOY-- THE SUPREME COUNCIL GAVE THEM A FREE HAND IF YOUR MISSION FAILED!

IN ANY CASE, WE'RE *JAMMING* THE VOSTRIAN DETECTION GEAR --TO COVER THEIR LANDING!

BUT AT THAT MOMENT--

I HAVE TRACKED THE CRAFT FROM THE MOMENT IT LEFT THE TERRAN STAR SHIP!

SO THE INTRUDERS ARE *EARTHLINGS!*

YOU'VE ALREADY COMMITTED AN ACT OF WAR BY TAKING US PRISONER! IF YOU PUT US ON TRIAL, IT'LL BE ANOTHER VIOLATION OF INTERPLANETARY LAW!

WHO IS THIS INSOLENT SCUM?

CAPTAIN PERDICARIS, EXCELLENCY --HE WAS *SKIPPER* OF THE TERRAN SHIP STEALING OUR SYNTHON!

SO MUCH THE BETTER! RACK HIM UP--AS A WARNING TO *ALL* GALACTIC PARASITES WHO COME TO *RAVAGE* OUR PLANET!

YOU HEARD THE REGENT! ACTIVATE THE *ELECTRO-RACK* AT ONCE!

BUCK ROGERS IN THE 25TH CENTURY ®

BUCK'S AND WILMA'S LANDING ON VOSTRIA SEEMS TO HAVE STIRRED UP A GIANT HORNET'S NEST!

IF THEY WERE PIGEONS, WE'D REALLY BE IN TROUBLE!

THE TWO EARTHLINGS TAKE HASTY REFUGE FROM THEIR WINGED ATTACKERS IN A ROCKY CLEFT OF THE HILLSIDE!

THEY'RE JUST CIRCLING NOW!

THEY'VE FOUND OUT WE CAN STING, TOO!

BUT ONE OF THE HORDE SEEMS DETERMINED TO PRESS HOME THE ASSAULT!

NO, BUCK--- DON'T FIRE!

THIS KAMIKAZE'S ASKING FOR IT!

THAT'S AN **ORDER** CAPTAIN--!

SHE'S MAKING A **TRUCE** SIGN!

WISELY DONE, TERRAN! HAD ANYTHING HAPPENED TO ME- **BOTH** YOUR LIVES WOULD HAVE BEEN FORFEIT!

SKIP THE THREATS! YOU WANTED A CHANCE TO PARLEY--OKAY, YOU'VE GOT IT!

OUR STARSHIP WAS SUPPOSED TO *JAM* THE VOSTRIAN WARNING SYSTEM!

PERHAPS IT DID --BUT WE HAVE OUR OWN DETECTOR --MANNED BY JANKOR HERE!

I TRACKED YOU IN! WE THOUGHT AT FIRST YOUR MISSION MIGHT BE SOME SORT OF *SECRET DEAL* WITH RAISULI!

NO WAY! WE CAME TO SPRING THE TERRAN HOSTAGES!

IF THAT MEANS TO *FREE* THEM, YOU'VE A LONG WAY TO GO! THEY'RE BEING HELD AT VOSTAR!

MY FATHER'S A PRISONER THERE, TOO! I'LL GUIDE YOU TO VOSTAR *PERSONALLY!*

A LITTLE REST MIGHT NOT HURT BEFORE WE START--VOSTAR'S ON THE OTHER SIDE OF THE PLANET!

GOOD IDEA--IF CAPTAIN ROGERS CAN TEAR HIMSELF AWAY FROM YOUR CHARMING GIRL GUERRILLAS!

LET ME FIND YOU A COMFORTABLE SPOT!

THE CAPTAIN'S A FOOL TO EVEN *LOOK* AT ANOTHER WOMAN --WHEN YOU'RE AROUND, LOVELY TERRAN!

BETTER TELL *HIM* THAT, JANKOR!

I'LL MAKE A NOTE OF IT! AND MAY I ADD-- HOW GRACEFULLY YOU YAWN, COLONEL!

ANY MORE CRACKS LIKE THAT ONE ABOUT HOW GRACEFULLY I YAWN--AND YOU COULD WIND UP A BUCK SPACEMAN!

SORRY, COLONEL! YOU CAN'T BUST ME --MY RANK'S ONLY HONORARY! BUT

IF LOOKS COULD KILL --SOMETHING TELLS ME I'D BE TURNING UP MY TOES RIGHT NOW!

LATER--AS THE GUERRILLA CAMP ROUSES---

HEAD FOR OUR SECRET BASE NEAR VOSTAR! FROM THERE THE TERRANS AND I WILL GO ON ALONE!

BUCK ROGERS IN THE 25TH CENTURY ®

THAT "HORNETS' NEST" HAS TURNED OUT TO BE A BAND OF FRIENDLY GUERRILLAS -- AS ANTI- THE POWER-MAD VOSTRIAN REGENT AS OUR TWO TERRAN SCOUTS!

GOOD LUCK EARTHLINGS!

THE GUERRILLA CHIEF, SYRENA, GUIDES BUCK AND WILMA TO A SAFE VANTAGE POINT -- FROM WHICH TO VIEW THE CAPITAL OF VOSTRIA!

FANTASTIC! A WHOLE CITY CANTILEVERED OUT FROM THE CLIFFSIDE!

NOT SO FANTASTIC -- CONSIDERING ITS INHABITANTS ARE WINGED!

THE SPACEPORT -- AS YOU SEE -- IS ON THE PLAIN BORDERING THE BAY!

IN A PRISON COMPOUND NEAR THE WATERFRONT IS WHERE THE HOSTAGES ARE BEING HELD PRISONER -- ALONG WITH MY FATHER, THE DEPOSED DEMOCRATIC RULER!

SO THAT'S OUR *TARGET FOR TONIGHT*, HUH?

BUCK AND WILMA ARE GETTING THEIR FIRST GLIMPSE OF VOSTAR -- WHERE THE HOSTAGES ARE BEING HELD CAPTIVE!

HOW TIGHTLY IS THE PRISON COMPOUND GUARDED, SYRENA?

USUALLY THERE ARE SOLDIERS POSTED BOTH ON THE ROOF AND AT STREET LEVEL -- BUT THE EXACT POSTING CHANGES DAILY!

THEN WE'D BETTER FIND OUT FOR SURE BEFORE WE STAGE ANY ASSAULT!

OKAY, COLONEL -- LEAVE THAT TO ME! I'LL SCOUT THE JOINT CLOSER AS SOON AS IT GETS DARK!

AS THE EARTHLINGS AND SYRENA REJOIN HER GUERRILLAS AT THEIR SECRET ADVANCE BASE NEAR THE VOSTRIAN CAPITAL --

I DON'T LIKE THE IDEA OF YOU SCOUTING THE PRISON COMPOUND *ALONE*, BUCK -- WE'LL GO TOGETHER!

NO WAY! IF WE BOTH GOT BAGGED -- THAT WOULD BLOW OUR RESCUE MISSION FOR KEEPS!

HE'S RIGHT! LET HIM PICK TWO OF MY GROUP AS WINGMEN! COME ON, CAPTAIN---

WILMA --?

ARE YOU ANGRY AT ME, LOVELY TERRAN -- FOR DARING TO CALL YOU 'WILMA' RATHER THAN 'COLONEL DEERING'?

ONE'S AS GOOD AS THE OTHER, JANKOR!

BUT PLEASE -- LET'S SKIP THE ROMANTIC BIT WHILE THIS OPERATION'S ON!

SORRY TO CUT IN, OLD BOY -- BUT I'D LIKE A WORD WITH THE COLONEL BEFORE TAKEOFF!

WHILE AT THE HQ OF THE REGENT'S DREADED SECRET POLICE ---

WATCH FOR ANY *SIGNAL* FROM THE GUERRILLA BASE!

69

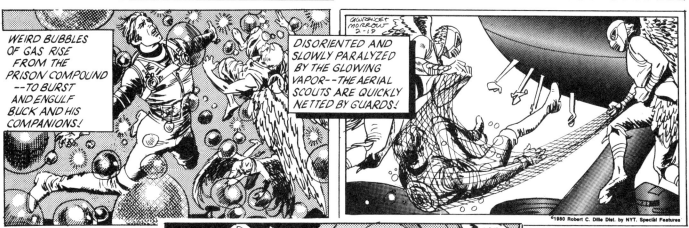

©1980 Robert C. Dille. Dist. by N.Y.T. Special Feature.

TIPPED OFF BY THE GUERRILLA WHO WAS TOLD TO WATCH JANKOR--WILMA AND SYRENA CATCH HIM COMMUNICATING WITH THE SECRET POLICE!

WHAT'S WRONG, JANKOR ... IS SOMEONE THERE?!

ER, N-N-NO ... NO ONE, COMMISSAR! I--I MUST BE GETTING JUMPY!

KEEP TALKING, TRAITOR! YOUR LIFE MAY DEPEND ON IT!

AS I WAS S-S-SAYING, COMMISSAR ... TH-THE TERRAN SPY SEEMS WILLING TO DEAL!

YOU HEARD ME, JANKOR! ... KEEP TALKING!

SHUT UP, JANKOR! WHAT KIND OF A FOOL DO YOU TAKE ME FOR?!

YOUR VOICE ANALYSIS SHOWS CLEARLY THAT YOU'RE SPEAKING UNDER PANIC STRESS!

AS FOR YOU, COLONEL DEERING--IF YOU WANT TO SEE CAPTAIN ROGERS OR THE OTHER HOSTAGES ---YOU'LL FIND THEM IN THE PALACE DUNGEON!

LOOK, WILMA, YOU KNOW HOW MUCH WE ALL WANT TO HELP! BUT I CAN'T WASTE LIVES ON A HOPELESS MISSION!

EVERY ONE OF US IS KNOWN TO THE SECRET POLICE!

THERE'S NO POSSIBLE WAY WE COULD GET INSIDE THE PALACE UNDETECTED-- TO FREE BUCK AND THE OTHER EARTHLINGS!

IF THERE WERE ANY WAY--DON'T YOU SUPPOSE I'D RESCUE MY OWN FATHER, THE RIGHTFUL RULER OF VOSTRIA?!

I UNDERSTAND, SYRENA--AND YOU'RE RIGHT! I'LL HAVE TO FREE THEM MYSELF!

WILMA, BE SERIOUS! HOW CAN YOU HOPE TO GET TO THE PALACE? WITHOUT BEING SPOTTED? ... YOU HAVEN'T EVEN WINGS!

MAYBE I CAN SPROUT A PAIR! BUT NEVER MIND THAT...

YOU'VE TOLD ME THAT RAISULI SEIZED POWER BY CONVINCING EVERYONE THAT YOUR FATHER WAS THE DEATH HAWK DEVIL-GOD REBORN!

TRUE--BUT SO WHAT?

OBVIOUSLY, THE ONLY WAY TO OVERTHROW RAISULI IS TO SHOW PEOPLE THAT HE HIMSELF IS THE REAL DEVIL-GOD!

BUCK ROGERS ® *IN THE 25TH CENTURY*

AT GRAVE RISK, WILMA'S HAD HERSELF TELEPORTED BACK TO THE STARSHIP CONSTITUTION -- HOVERING NEAR THE PLANET VOSTRIA!

THANK HEAVENS! STILL IN *ONE* PIECE!

HAD OUR BEAM BEEN INTERCEPTED, YOU REALIZE YOU MIGHT'VE ARRIVED HERE LOOKING LIKE A *SCRAMBLED JIGSAW PUZZLE!*

FIRST OF ALL, THANKS FOR COMING HERE FROM EARTH ON SUCH SHORT NOTICE, DR. HUER!

-- AND FOR TAKING THE GAMBLE TO TELEPORT ME UP FROM THE SURFACE OF VOSTRIA!

IT WAS THE ONLY WAY I HAD ANY CHANCE OF GETTING BACK TO THE SHIP UNDETECTED!

WHAT'S ALL THIS ABOUT BUCK BEING CAPTURED BY THE REGENT'S SECRET POLICE, WILMA?!

THAT'S WHY I CALLED YOU! BY THE WAY -- YOU CAME IN *STARLAB?*

OF COURSE! YOU TOLD ME TO BRING A FULL RANGE OF SCIENTIFIC GEAR!

GOOD! LET ME BRIEF YOU FAST ON HOW THE REGENT RAISULI GRABBED POWER!

VOSTRIA SUFFERED A REIGN OF TERROR FROM SQUADS OF BULLIES CALLED *DEATH HAWKS!*

LAWRENCE & MORROW 3-9

RAISULI CONVINCED EVERYONE THEY WERE SECRET AGENTS SENT OUT BY THE ELECTED RULER, HATHOR.

-- AND THAT HATHOR HIMSELF WAS THE ANCIENT *DEATH HAWK* DEVIL-GOD REBORN!

SO TO OVERTHROW THE TYRANT RAISULI -- THE PEOPLE MUST BE SHOWN THAT HE, HIMSELF, IS THE REAL DEATH HAWK!

RIGHT! TO DO THAT, I'LL NEED A LASER HOLOGRAM -- AND TO RESCUE BUCK, A PAIR OF *WINGS!*

THE PEOPLE ARE IN A FRENZY, SIRE!--OVER THAT HUGE, GHASTLY DEATH HAWK IN THE SKY!

CALL MY AIDE! HE IS FETCHING HATHOR FROM THE DUNGEON! TELL HIM TO HURRY!

AT THAT MOMENT--

DROP YOUR GUN, WENCH!

TAKE HER WEAPON, COMMISSAR, WHILE I ANSWER THE VIDEO-COM! THIS MAY BE FROM THE REGENT!

TELL THE REGENT I'VE FOUND COMMISSAR KROL! HE WAS BEING FORCED AT GUNPOINT TO FREE THE PRISONERS!

AND WITH HIS CAPTOR'S ATTENTION MOMENTARILY DIVERTED, BUCK'S HAND DARTS OUT---!

NOW'S MY CHANCE --!

WHILE ABOARD THE TERRAN STARSHIP---

AS OUR FRIEND CAPTAIN ROGERS WOULD SAY--THOSE VOSTRIANS AIN'T SEEN NUTHIN' YET--!

I'LL EXPLAIN LATER-- AS SOON AS THIS SITUATION IN THE DUNGEON HAS BEEN DEALT WITH!

COMMISSAR KROL HAS SEEN BUCK'S SUDDEN MOVE! BUT BEFORE HE CAN REACT---

MEANWHILE--

WHAT NOW, DR. HUER?

THE DEATH HAWK IS ABOUT TO GET A NEW IMAGE!

THAT GIANT DEATH HAWK IN THE SKY NOW LOOKS LIKE THE REGENT RAISULI!

THE GODS ARE SHOWING US THE TRUTH!

RAISULI IS THE **EVIL** ONE WHO SPREAD TERROR OVER THE LAND --**NOT** HATHOR!

WHILE ON THE PALACE BALCONY--

ARE YOU MAD?! WHY WOULD COMMISSAR KROL BE FREEING THE PRISONERS?!

AN ATTEMPTED JAILBREAK, SIRE-- BUT IT'S BEEN THWARTED!

YOUR AIDE SAYS HE WILL REPORT MORE FULLY WHEN HE RETURNS FROM THE DUNGEONS!

DOES THAT FOOL OF AN AIDE THINK THE MOB WILL HOLD OFF TILL HE RETURNS FROM THE DUNGEON?! **CALL OUT THE GUARDS!**

OF C-COURSE SIRE! AT ONCE!

MEANWHILE...

ALL RIGHT, BUCK--I HAVE THESE TWO COVERED!

GET THE COMMISSAR UP ON HIS FEET! WE MAY NEED HIM TO GET OUT OF THE PALACE ALIVE!

WAIT! HEAR ME, PLEASE!

THE GUARD CAPTAIN KNEELS BEFORE HATHOR---

IF YOU WILL TRUST ME, SIRE, YOU NEED NOT FLEE LIKE AN ESCAPING FELON!

WHAT ARE YOU PROPOSING?

THAT YOU TAKE OVER THE PALACE! THE GUARDS WILL SUPPORT YOU! WE HAVE HAD ENOUGH OF RAISULI'S MISRULE!

WHY SHOULD ANYONE TRUST YOU, BUSTER?

A FAIR QUESTION! NEVERTHELESS, I DO TRUST HIM!

THANKS TO YOU TERRANS, VOSTRIA NOW HAS A CHANCE TO REGAIN ITS FREEDOM! LET US SEIZE THAT CHANCE!

As the escapees make their way out of the palace dungeon, Wilma hastily briefs her companions---

LAWRENCE MORROW 3-27

With luck, that giant hologram in the sky should turn the people in your favor, Excellency!

Sounds almost like a miracle!

Your daughter performed the real miracle! Syrena's fighters kept freedom alive on Yostria while you were in Raisuli's power!

Don't get me wrong, gang, but we're not quite out of his power yet!

The grim sky image and Syrena's freedom-fighters have stirred the people of Yostria to open rebellion!

There's your real death hawk!

Down with Raisuli!

Guards! Guards!! ...Confound the fools, where are they when I need them?!

Suddenly the palace doors burst open --and the guards rush out on the balcony!

Here at last, are you?! ...Fire on this rebel scum!

You'll be seeing your daughter soon! But please --wait inside, your Excellency!

You mean Syrena herself is leading an attack on the palace?!

It figures! Let the guards cope with Raisuli before you show yourself on the balcony!

Didn't you hear me, you dogs!? I said-- Fire!!

If we fire at all, Raisuli --it won't be at the people! It'll be at you!

LAWRENCE MORROW 3-29

PRO. Robert C. Dille Dist. by N.Y. Special Feat.

87

WHILE BUCK AND WILMA ZOOM UP TO THE TERRAN STARSHIP THAT BROUGHT THEM TO VOSTRIA---

--LET'S LOOK IN ON A PRIMITIVE PLANET CALLED TEXAR--WHERE RANCHER-COLONISTS RAISE A BREED OF CATTLE CALLED URGOTHS...

-- AND A MOTLEY HORDE OF TOUGH HOMBRES FROM ALL OVER THE GALAXY RAISE *CAIN!

*OR SHOULD THAT BE SPELLED 'KANE' AS IN KILLER'?

ON THE PLANET TEXAR--A FABULOUS METAL STRIKE...

YIPPEEE! PURE SCINTILLIUM!

...HAS BROUGHT A FLOOD OF LAWLESS ADVENTURERS AND PROSPECTORS POURING IN FROM THE STARLANES!

LOOK AT THEM! HOW CAN ANYONE FEEL SAFE HERE ANY MORE?

GATE 1

MEANWHILE---

WILMA! BUCK! GREAT JOB YOU DID ON VOSTRIA!

BUT NOW IT SEEMS--THERE'S AN EVEN MORE DANGEROUS JOB TO BE DONE ON TEXAR!

YOU'LL HAVE TO EXCUSE MY TWENTIETH CENTURY IGNORANCE, FOLKS-- BUT WHAT'S TEXAR?

YOU MIGHT SAY IT'S A PLANET READY TO EXPLODE, BUCK! BUT NEVER MIND! THAT NOW ---

FOR THE MOMENT--LET'S JUST CELEBRATE THE LIBERATION OF VOSTRIA!

ONCE WE'RE BACK IN NEW CHICAGO WILL BE TIME ENOUGH TO HEAR THE BAD NEWS!

BUCK ROGERS ®
IN THE 25th CENTURY

LOOKS LIKE A WILD AND WOOLY PLACE, THIS PLANET OF TEXAR!

MUCH LIKE THE WILD WEST OF YOUR OWN TIME, BUCK!

DR. HUER PAINTS A GRIM PICTURE OF CONDITIONS ON EARTH'S DISTANT FRONTIER COLONY...

LAW AND ORDER HAVE COMPLETELY BROKEN DOWN ON TEXAR!

BECAUSE OF THE SCINTILLIUM STRIKE?

Y'MEAN THE PLANET'S TURNING INTO A *LAWLESS MINING CAMP?*

EXACTLY! PROSPECTORS ARE STREAMING THERE FROM ALL OVER THE GALAXY!

OUTLAWS ARE GROWING BOLDER ... ONE, CALLED THE *FACELESS KID*, HAS GUNNED DOWN OUR LOCAL PEACE OFFICER!

OUR STOCK RANCHERS ARE HELPLESS--AND WE SIMPLY HAVEN'T THE MANPOWER TO STATION A MILITARY UNIT ON THE PLANET!

SO--WHY ARE YOU TELLING ME THIS, DOC?

I'M HOPING YOU CAN BRING THE SITUATION UNDER CONTROL, BUCK!

LAWRENCE + MORROW 4-6

THAT'S WHY THE EARTH FEDERATION IS APPOINTING YOU--THE *MARSHAL OF TEXAR!*

92

WHAT'S THE EMERGENCY?

A SKY-TRAIN SHIPMENT OF SCINTILLIUM! THE OTHER DEPUTY GOT CALLED TO GUARD IT... I'M HOLDING DOWN THE OFFICE!

AT THAT VERY MOMENT--THE SKY-TRAIN WITH ITS PRECIOUS CARGO IS ROARING ACROSS THE TEXAR BADLANDS!

NO TROUBLE SO FAR!

WE AIN'T HOME SAFE YET, DEPUTY! IF ANY BUSHWHACKER'S LAYIN' FER US, IT'LL BE T'OTHER SIDE OF THE PASS-- OVER DEAD MAN'S GULCH!!

AS THE SKY-TRAIN EMERGES FROM THE PASS...

STOP THE TRAIN!!

OUTLAWS!

ON BUZZ-BRONCS!

THE DEPUTY'S LASER BLAST BRINGS A TERRIFYING RESPONSE!

GREAT SNAKES! IT'S THE FACELESS KID!

HOW DO I GET TO THE MAIN SETTLEMENT?

SCINTILLA-VILLE?.. TAKE THE SKY-RAIL-- A BUZZ BRONC -- OR A HORSE FROM THE LIVERY STABLE! I'LL DELIVER YOUR GEAR!

THAT'S A HORSE?!

ER-- THANKS, MAYBE A WALK WOULD BE GOOD EXERCISE!

DRILL HIM, DEPUTY!

I CAN'T! I CAN'T EVEN SEE HIM!

BUCK ROGERS ®
IN THE 25TH CENTURY

CAN BUCK BRING LAW AND ORDER TO THE EARTH'S WIDE-OPEN FRONTIER COLONY ON THE PLANET TEXAR?

THERE GOES OUR NEW MARSHAL! | HEAR HE JUST BLASTED IN FROM CHICAGO!

THE MARSHAL OF TEXAR'S FIRST IMPRESSIONS OF HIS NEW JOB AREN'T TOO ENCOURAGING...

WHAT DO YOU MEAN, THE OTHER DEPUTY MAY NOT BE BACK?

LIKE I SAID, HE'S RIDING LASER ON A BULLION SHIPMENT FROM THE ACE SCINTILLIUM MINE!

SO?

THE BOYS AT THE DOG-STAR SALOON ARE LAYIN' TEN TO ONE THAT BULLION'LL NEVER REACH THE SPACEPORT!

BZ-Z-T!

DEPUTY DORGAN HERE! WHAT'S UP?

PLENTY! THAT SKY-TRAIN BRINGING IN THE SCINTILLIUM SHIPMENT FROM THE ACE MINE GOT PRANGED OVER DEADMAN'S GULCH!

WHAT ABOUT THE LAWMAN WHO WAS GUARDING IT?

HE'S IN NO SHAPE TO FILE ANY REPORT! LOOKS LIKE HE MADE THE MISTAKE OF TANGLIN' WITH THE *FACELESS KID!*

1980 Robert C. Dille Dist. by NYT. Special Features

BUCK ARRIVES AT THE MARSHAL'S OFFICE ON TEXAR JUST AS WORD COMES IN OF THE SKY-TRAIN HOLDUP!

DEADMAN'S GULCH, EH?... OKAY, BE RIGHT THERE!

YOU SAVVY NOW WHY I SAID THERE WAS AN EMERGENCY?

NEVER MIND ALL THAT! IF THEY SHOT YOUR PARTNER, I'LL NEED SOMEONE TO SHOW ME THE WAY.

YOU'RE THE ONLY DEPUTY I'VE GOT LEFT--SO LOCK UP AND LET'S GO!

CORRECTION, MARSHAL! AS OF NOW, YOU AIN'T GOT *NO* DEPUTY LEFT!

YOU THE NEW MARSHAL?

I DIDN'T GET THIS STAR OUT OF A BOX OF KORN KRACKLIES! WHAT'S THE STORY ON THE SCINTILLIUM ROBBERY?

AT THE HOLD-UP SITE---

YOU CAN SEE WHAT HAPPENED TO THE SKY-TRAIN! THE GANG UNLOADED THE ORE AND TOOK OFF!

WHERE'S THE GUARD WHO GOT SHOT?

WE TOOK HIM TO THE SKY-LINE SHACK UP THE CANYON!

THERE'S YOUR DEPUTY!

GOOD GRIEF! LOOKS LIKE HE JUST GOT A PEEK AT THE PHANTOM OF THE OPERA!

AIN'T NO OPERA ON TEXAR, MARSHAL! WHAT SCARED HIM WAS THE SIGHT OF THE FACELESS KID!

YOU'RE THE TRAIN ENGINEER--RIGHT? OKAY, TELL ME WHAT *YOU* SAW!

AT FIRST THE GANG-LEADER'S FACE WAS JUST MISTY-BLANK--LIKE A GHOST! THEN IT STARTED TO *GLOW* AND BUST OUT IN *FLAMES!* I TURNED AWAY... THE DEPUTY DIDN'T... I HEARD HIM *SCREAM* --!

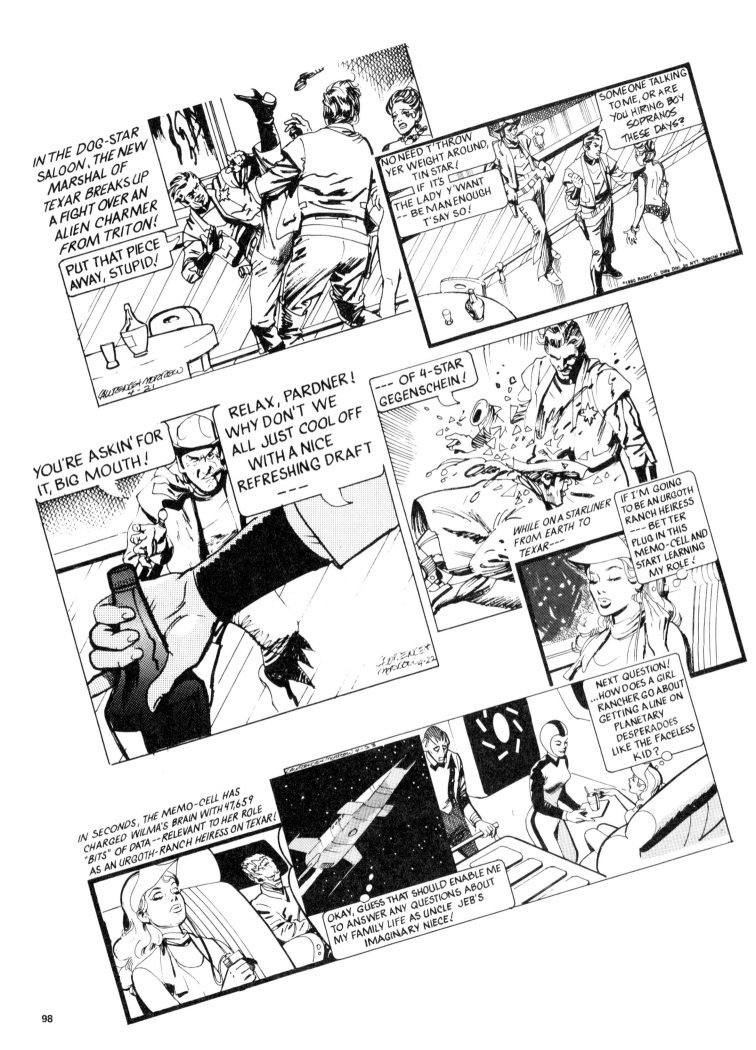

AND BUCK DOES A STARTLED DOUBLE-TAKE!

I'M SURE I'D *NEVER* FORGET A MAN LIKE *YOU*, MARSHAL--IF WE *HAD* MET BEFORE!

RECKON IT WAS JUST WISHFUL THINKING ON MY PART, MA'AM!

CALL ME *TYGRA!*

WELL, SEE YA 'ROUND--ER, TYGRA! GOTTA GO ENFORCE A FEW LAWS!

YOU DO THAT, BUCKY DEAR! AND I'LL START TURNING OVER ROCKS--TILL I FIND YOUR BLONDE SIDEKICK, WILMA!

LATER---

ARDALA ON *TEXAR!* ARE YOU *SURE*, BUCK?!

99%! WHICH MEANS *KILLER KANE* COULD BE BACK OF THE CRIME WAVE ON THIS FREAKED--OUT PLANET!

THE BETA X FOREMAN'S DRIVING WILMA TO HER LATE "UNCLE'S" URGOTH RANCH!...

QUITE--UH, *SPIRITED ANIMALS!* MORE LIKE ANTELOPES THAN HORSES!

YEP! THAT'S WHY THIS REPELLO-RAY BUGGY'S A DANG SIGHT EASIER ON THE SPINE THAN WHEELS!

WHILE BACK AT THE SPACEPORT...

BLONDE--STUCKUP--I SUPPOSE *SOME* MEN MIGHT CALL HER ATTRACTIVE...!

GATE V

SEEN ANYONE LIKE THAT LAND ON TEXAR LATELY?

HOW COULD I MISS HER? SHE'S THE NEW BOSS LADY OF THE BETA X SPREAD!

HOWDY--UH, LILY BELLE, ISN'T IT?

WHAT'S IT T'YOU, MARSHAL? I THOUGHT TYGRA WAS MORE YOUR TYPE!

LAWMAN'S GOTTA GET AQUAINTED, MA'AM! HAD A HUNCH I'D SEEN HER ON THE INTER-PLANETARY WANTED LIST!

...HAS SHE ANY GENTLEMEN FRIENDS?

LISTEN, TINSTAR! ANY FRIEND OF TYGRA'S NO GENTLEMAN!

BUT SINCE YOU ASK-- SHE BLEW INTA *SCINTILLA-VILLE* WITH SOME *TALL DARK STRANGER!*

AND SHE'S BEEN KEEPING HIM UNDER WRAPS EVER SINCE--FOR FEAR HE MIGHT GET AN EYEFUL OF *ME!*

WILMA COMES TO IN STRANGE SURROUNDINGS...

WH-WHERE AM I?

AMONG FRIENDS, HONEY!

KILLER KANE!

BRING HER SOME BREAKFAST, GORGEOUS... I'LL KEEP AN EYE ON OUR GUEST!

TIME YOU AND I GOT ACQUAINTED, BABY!

NOT IF I CAN HELP IT--!

WHILE BACK IN SCINTILLA-VILLE...

NOW HEAR THIS! OUR NEW TIN-STAR'S CALLING THE FACELESS KID YELLOW!

MAN, WAIT'LL KANE SEES THIS!

I LIKED YOU BETTER FACELESS, KANE!

OH YEAH? MAYBE YOU'VE FORGOT WHAT HAPPENED T'YA--WHEN YA TRIED DRAWIN' ON THE FACELESS KID!

YOUR PERSONALITY BY ITSELF MADE ME SICK--LET ALONE YOUR LOOKS!

WRONG, COLONEL! HERE'S WHAT DID IT! KEEP ON LIKE THIS AND YOU'LL GET THE SAME TREATMENT AGAIN!

HEY, BOSS--

YEAH?

'THREE FINGERS' IS HERE!

STICK AROUND, 'THREE FINGERS' -- WHILE I SHOW THIS TO HER LADYSHIP, THE COLONEL!

YOU THINK IT'S FUNNY?

A LAUGH RIOT, BABY!

CAN YOU IMAGINE THAT DUMB JET JOCKEY-- ITCHIN' T'TRY HIS DRAW AGAINST THE *FACELESS KID!*

THE MARSHALL MIGHT JUST SURPRISE YOU, KANE!

HE'S THE ONE WHO'LL GET A SURPRISE--WHEN I GIVE HIM A BLAST FROM *THIS!*

SHREWD THINKING, KANE! IT'S REAL SMART OF YOU TO WEAR THAT 'FACELESS' GIMMICK AROUND YOUR THROAT-- WHATEVER IT IS!

NOW HE'S GONNA GET' WHAT'S COMING TO HIM!

THEN I'LL COME BACK AND ATTEND TO *YOU!*

YOU'LL NEED ALL THE EDGE YOU CAN GET-- WHEN YOU GO UP AGAINST *BUCK ROGERS!*

LISTEN, BABY-- YOU GOT A LOT T'LEARN!

THAT WIMP THOUGHT HE HAD ME AND ARDALA EXILED T' THE ANDROMEDA NEBULA FOR KEEPS!

KEEP AN EYE ON HER, GORGEOUS! SHE MAY TRY SOMETHING CUTE!

WHERE YA GOIN' BOSS?

TO TOWN-- T'TAKE CARE OF THAT JOKER WHO CALLS HIMSELF MARSHAL OF TEXAR!

FLASH WORD TO ALL THE GANG! THEY MAY WANTA SEE THIS!

BUCK ROGERS IN THE 25TH CENTURY

THE GRUB SERVED AT KILLER KANE'S HIDE-OUT SEEMS TO BE DISAGREEING NOT ONLY WITH WILMA, BUT WITH 'GORGEOUS' THE COOK!

A REAL TASTE SENSATION! ... RIGHT?

GIVE THAT LITTLE LADY A--*BIG HAND!*

AS THE BURLY GUARD LUNGES AT HER TROUBLESOME PRISONER--WILMA DEFTLY CHOPS HER DOWN TO SIZE!

BY THIS TIME, THINGS ARE GETTING A LITTLE NOISY--

HEY! WHAT'S GOIN' ON IN THERE--?!

ASK A FOOLISH QUESTION-- *YOU KNOW THE REST!*

MEANWHILE--KILLER KANE IS ZOOMING TO SCINTILLA-VILLE FOR A SHOWDOWN WITH MARSHAL BUCK ROGERS!

GONNA HAVE SOME FUN FIRST-- OR JUST BLOW HIM AWAY?

YOU KNOW ME, THREE FINGERS-- I'M STRICTLY A FUN GUY!

SO FIRST I'LL GIVE HIM A *GOOD LOOK* AT THE FACELESS KID!

WILMA TRIPS AN OUTLAW WHO RUSHES IN TO INVESTIGATE THE NOISE-- THEN TURNS TO DEAL WITH GORGEOUS AGAIN!

DOWN, GIRL!

EXCUSE ME IF I DON'T STOP TO CHAT! 'FRAID I'LL HAVE TO USE YOUR TELE-COM GEAR! D' YOU MIND?

YOU DO? ...OH GOSH, I'M SORRY--!

NO TIME TO EXPLAIN, DR. HUER-- BUT I'M AT THE FACELESS KID'S HIDEOUT!

YOU'VE SEEN THE KID HIMSELF?

HE'S ACTUALLY OUR OLD ACQUAINTANCE-- KILLER KANE!

BUT HE WEARS SOME *MYSTERIOUS GADGET* AROUND HIS NECK--THAT SOMEHOW KEEPS YOU FROM SEEING HIS FACE!

...IN FACT, IT *FREAKS ME OUT!*

THIS DEVICE KANE WEARS-- WHAT ARE THE *EXACT SYMPTOMS* IT PRODUCES ON A VICTIM?

BLURRED VISION-- THEN DIZZINESS THAT INCREASES TO A BLINDING HEADACHE!

BY THIS TIME, HIS HEAD ISN'T JUST BLURRED-- HIS HEAD LOOK AS IF IT'S *GLOWING!*

THEN IT SEEMS TO BURST INTO *FLAME*-- AND YOU *PASS OUT* FROM PAIN!

HMM...FROM THE CLINICAL PICTURE YOU DESCRIBE, WILMA-- I'D SAY THERE'S ONLY *ONE POSSIBLE EXPLANATION!*

WHAT'S THE ANSWER, DOCTOR?... HOW DOES KANE PULL HIS 'FACELESS KID' ACT?

AS YOU DESCRIBE THEM, WILMA-- THE SYMPTONS ARE ALL *SUB*JECTIVE... THAT IS, THEY EXIST ONLY IN THE VICTIM'S *MIND!*

THEN YOU'RE SAYING, THE SECRET WEAPON GIMMICK THAT KANE WEARS AROUND HIS NECK--

--MUST BE A *BRAIN-WAVE DISTORTER!*

I COULD TELL YOU HOW TO *GET* THE FACELESS KID!...WE COULD EVEN *TAKE OVER* THIS PLANET, BUCK!

...IF YOU PLAY YOUR CARDS RIGHT!

WHY NOT JUST LAY 'EM ON THE TABLE?... I KNOW YOU'RE ARDALA --AND HE'S KANE! ...WHAT MORE DO I NEED?

LOTSA LUCK, MARSHAL-- 'CAUSE THE KID'S HERE NOW!

BUCK CHALLENGED THE FACELESS KID TO A SHOOTOUT! IT COULD BE HAPPENING RIGHT NOW!

GOOD LORD! WITH NO PROTECTION AGAINST KANE'S BRAIN-WAVE DISTORTER--

BUCK WON'T STAND A CHANCE!

YOU'RE TELLING ME!

'SMATTER, TIN STAR?... YOU WERE DARING THE FACELESS KID T'SHOW UP IN TOWN-- WELL, HERE I AM!...SUMTHIN' YOU WANTED T'SEE ME ABOUT?

DON'T LOOK LIKE THE MARSHAL'S FEELIN' TOO GOOD, KID!

WHAT DID YOU *DO* TO HIM, TYGRA?! I DUNNO WHAT YOUR GAME IS-- BUT *YOU* SET THE TIN STAR UP!

WRONG, LILY BELLE DEAR! YOU AND SAL SET THE WHOLE THING UP WITH THOSE POSTERS YOU HANDED OUT!

ME, I *WANTED* T' HELP-- BUT MARSHAL ROGERS DIDN'T LIKE WHAT I HAD TO OFFER!

BUCK'S HEAD THROBS WITH PAIN AS HE SQUINTS HELPLESSLY AT THE DAZZLING FIGURE OF HIS OUTLAW-ENEMY!

IT'S AS IF HE'S RADIATING LIGHT!--AND EVERY RAY'S A RED-HOT NEEDLE!

AT THAT MOMENT--

WHERE'S THE NEW MARSHAL?

AIN'T Y'HEARD? HIM AND THE FACELESS KID ARE ALL SET TO SLAP LEATHER OVER AT THE DOG-STAR SALOON!

BETTER HURRY IF Y'AIM T' SEE HIM, HONEY! LATEST ODDS ARE 10-TO-1 IT'S THE TIN STAR WHO'LL WIND UP IN BOOT HILL!

EVERYONE IN SCINTILLA-VILLE'S RUSHING TO SEE THE SHOWDOWN BETWEEN THE PLANET'S NEW MARSHAL AND THE FACELESS KID!

WILMA HESITATES ONLY LONG ENOUGH TO FIGURE THE FASTEST WAY TO THE SCENE-- THEN LEAPS BACK ASTRIDE HER BUZZ-BRONC---!

--AND ZOOMS OVER THE HEADS OF THE CROWD STRAIGHT TOWARD THE DOG-STAR SALOON!

116

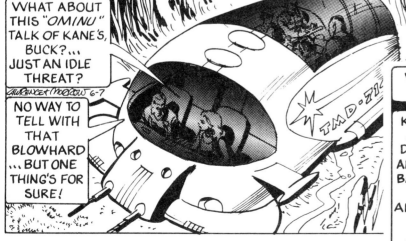

YOU'VE NO IDEA *HOW* AN ENEMY COULD CAUSE ALL THOSE SUNSPOTS?

NO BUCK-- WE'VE STILL MUCH TO LEARN ABOUT SOLAR PHYSICS!

BUT YOU ASSUME HE MUST BE OPERATING INSIDE OUR SOLAR SYSTEM?

OR NEAR IT! BUT PROBABLY ON THE OTHER SIDE OF THE SUN--WHICH MAKES HIM DIFFICULT TO DETECT!

©1980 Robert C. Dille Dist. by NYT. Special Features

SO A-HUNTING WE WILL GO --EH, DOC?

QUITE RIGHT, MY BOY! I'VE HAD THE NEW *STARLAB* SPECIALLY FITTED FOR A SUN CRUISE!

HOW CLOSE TO THE SUN WILL OUR SHIELDING PROTECT US, DR. HUER?

I'M AFRAID NO COMPUTER CAN REALLY PREDICT THAT, WILMA---

WE'LL HAVE TO RELY ON OUR INSTRUMENTATION! AND LET'S FACE IT --THAT *MAY* NOT GIVE US ADEQUATE WARNING!

OKAY, THEN-- HEADS UP, YOU TWO! HERE'S A WARNING RIGHT NOW-- WE'VE GOT *COMPANY!*

ANOTHER SPACECRAFT?

THIS CLOSE TO THE SUN?!

AFFIRMATIVE!

ITS POSITION ALONE ALMOST CONFIRMS YOUR SUSPICIONS, DR. HUER!

PERHAPS! ... BEFORE WE JUMP TO ANY CONCLUSIONS, LET'S SEE HOW IT RESPONDS TO A GALACTIC CONTACT CALL!

CRUISING CLOSE TO TERRA'S MOTHER STAR
-- THE SUN-- TO INVESTIGATE RECENT INTENSE
SUNSPOT ACTIVITY --STARLAB ENCOUNTERS
A LURKING MYSTERY CRAFT ....!

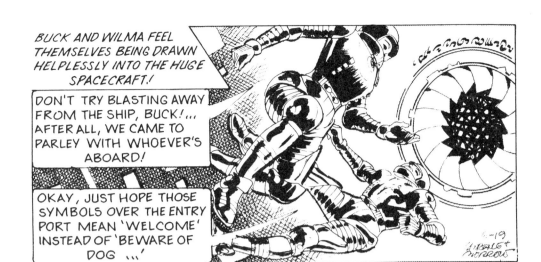

IS IT OKAY TO ASK WHERE THE HIGH AND MIGHTY OMINU HIMSELF CAME FROM?

BY ALL MEANS, CAPTAIN -- YOUR QUESTION IS PERFECTLY IN ORDER!

IN THE BEGINNING OF THE COSMOS-- *ONE WORLD* EMERGED FROM NOTHINGNESS--AND FROM THIS WORLD, *MY RACE* WAS BORN!

BUT IN TIME, OUR STAR GREW COLD-- AND WE YEARNED FOR *NEW WORLDS* TO REFLECT OUR GLORY!

980 Robert C. Dille Dist. by NYT. Special Features

THESE NEW WORLDS YOUR RACE GOT A YEN FOR--WOULD THEY INCLUDE OUR EARTH?

YOUR EARTH?! ...COME, COME, MY SON!

SURELY YOU MUST REALIZE --EVEN WITH YOUR LIMITED COMPREHENSION--THAT YOUR EARTH, YOUR SUN AND ALL ITS PLANETS-- ALREADY BELONG TO *OMINU!*

OUR EARTH--OUR SUN--OUR WHOLE SOLAR SYSTEM --ALREADY BELONG TO OMINU?

STAKING OUT A PRETTY BIG CLAIM, ISN'T HE?

'CLAIM' DID YOU SAY? BUT WHAT ELSE WOULD YOU EXPECT ---

---WHEN THEY ALL SPRANG FROM THE MINDS OF OMINU AND HIS RACE!

INDEED THE VAST UNIVERSE ITSELF IS OUR CREATION!

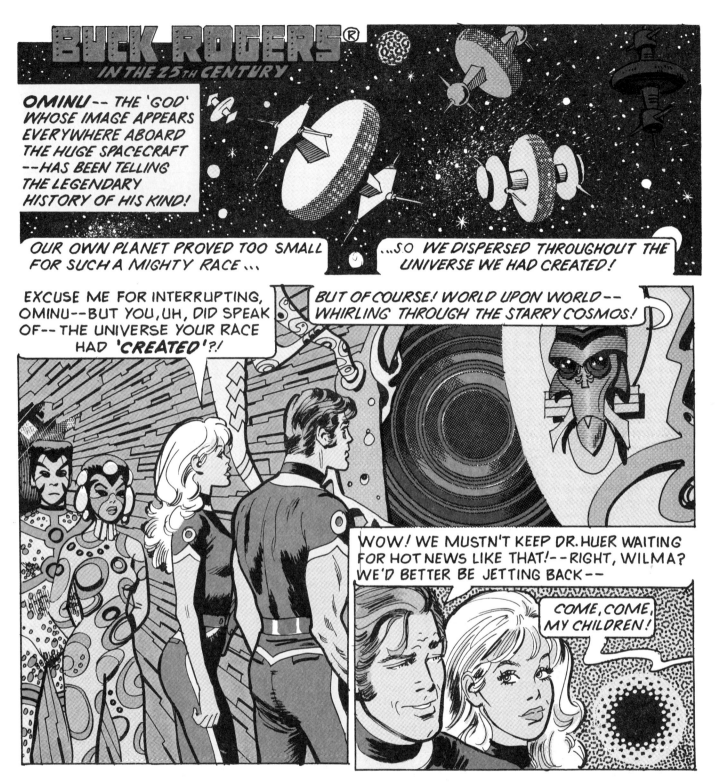

OMINU-- SELF-STYLED CREATOR OF THE UNIVERSE--
INSISTS THAT BUCK AND WILMA STAY ABOARD LONGER
TO "ENJOY OUR HOSPITALITY"...!

ARE YOU TELLING US WE'RE PRISONERS?

BY NO MEANS, CAPTAIN ROGERS! PLEASE THINK OF YOURSELVES AS OUR *GUESTS*!

NYALA AND TARK WILL PERSONALLY UNDERTAKE TO MAKE YOUR VISIT TO OUR LITTLE WORLD AS AGREEABLE AS POSSIBLE!

THE EARTHLINGS ARE GIVEN A GUIDED TOUR OF OMINU'S AMAZING STARSHIP...

OUR OBSERVATORY GEAR CAN BEND LIGHT RAYS-- TO ENABLE US TO PEER INTO THE REMOTEST CORNER OF YOUR GALAXY!

ENOUGH, TARK! OUR GUESTS NEED A REST -- AND A CHANCE TO CHANGE INTO MORE COMFORTABLE GARMENTS!

HOW'LL WE EVER GET AWAY FROM HERE, BUCK?!

AN EMERGENCY MIGHT HELP -- IF WE CAN PANIC OUR GENIAL HOSTS OFF-GUARD!

IF YOU'VE RESTED, MAY I HELP YOU CHANGE INTO SOMETHING MORE COMFORTABLE?

ER--NO THANKS! IF YOU DID, I MIGHT CHANGE INTO SOMETHING MORE THAN YOU COULD HANDLE! BESIDES, WE TERRANS ARE RATHER MODEST...

OF COURSE! OMINU FORESAW AS MUCH... HENCE HE WITHHELD HIS PRESENCE FROM THESE GUEST CHAMBERS!

THOUGHTFUL OF HIM!

7-2

AFTER CHANGING--BUCK TAKES OUT A POCKET TOOL ISSUED TO ALL TERRAN SPACEMEN---

HANDY LITTLE GIZMOS, THESE *LASER GENIES* -- ESPECIALLY WHEN YOU HAVEN'T GOT A BOY SCOUT TO RUB TWO STICKS TOGETHER!

©1980 Robert C. Dille Dist. by NYT. Special Features

ONE OF OMINU'S PEOPLE WAS BURNED IN PUTTING OUT THE FIRE-- YET SHE SHOWS NO PAIN--AND HER BURNS ARE INSTANTLY HEALED IN THE SPACESHIP'S SICK BAY!

DO NOT LOOK SO ALARMED, MY FRIENDS!... YOU SEE? NO HARM HAS BEEN DONE!

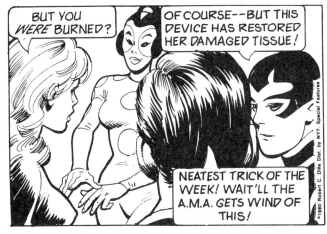

BUT YOU WERE BURNED?

OF COURSE--BUT THIS DEVICE HAS RESTORED HER DAMAGED TISSUE!

NEATEST TRICK OF THE WEEK! WAIT'LL THE A.M.A. GETS WIND OF THIS!

©1980 Robert C. Dille Dist. by NYT Special Features

COME! THE FIRE IS OUT AND AYUMA'S ARMS ARE WELL AGAIN--SO LET US ENJOY OURSELVES!

LATER---

WHY SO PENSIVE, BUCK?

CALL IT A SLIGHT CASE OF CULTURE SHOCK... I STILL DON'T SAVVY HOW AYUMA GOT OVER HER BURNS SO FAST!

THINK YOU COULD EXPLAIN THAT TO A DULL-WITTED EARTHLING LIKE ME?

DIDN'T AYUMA FEEL ANY PAIN?

NONE! OUR RACE WAS BRED TO ELIMINATE SUCH CRIPPLING EMOTIONAL RESPONSES!

BUT HOW COULD HER BURNT TISSUES HEAL SO FAST?... DON'T TELL ME YOU WERE ALSO BRED WITH MIRACULOUS BODY CELLS!

TO OUR LORD AND MASTER, OMINU--NOTHING IS IMPOSSIBLE!

MEANWHILE...

BEING SO LOVELY YOURSELF-- PERHAPS YOU WOULD CARE TO SEE THE BEAUTIFUL PLANT LIFE OUR MASTER HAS CREATED!

131

BUCK ROGERS®
IN THE 25TH CENTURY

IS ANYTHING WRONG, BUCK?

NOT WITH YOU, DEAR!...JUST REMEMBERED A SMALL--ER, MISSION DETAIL I HAVE TO CHECK OUT WITH COLONEL DEERING!

I GOT YOUR S.O.S. BEEP! ...WHAT HAPPENED?

TARK SEEMED TO THINK HIS HOSTLY DUTIES INCLUDED MAKING LOVE TO ME!

SO YOU COOLED HIM OFF WITH A DEMONSTRATION OF THE MARTIAL ARTS!

HE LANDED HARD--AGAINST A SHARP POINT OF THIS WEIRD PLANT!

YOU MEAN, HE'S DEAD?

NOT REALLY---

JUST HIS CYBERTRONIC CIRCUITS!

HOLY HOLOGRAMS!...AN ANDROID!

LAWRENCE & MORROW 7-13

WILMA'S PUT-DOWN OF TARK LEADS TO A STRANGE DISCOVERY!

ELECTRONIC SPAGHETTI! ... NO WONDER AYUMA'S ARMS COULD BE REPAIRED SO FAST--IF THEY'RE ALL JUST *ROBOTS*!

BUT SUCH LIFELIKE SPECIMENS --IT'S INCREDIBLE! SURELY THEY MUST BE AT LEAST *PARTLY BIOLOGICAL ANDROIDS*!

QUITE RIGHT, MY DEAR--BUT YOU NEED NOT WORRY! I SHALL HAVE TARK *SURGICALLY REGENERATED* AT ONCE!

THE INJURED ANDROID SOON RISES FROM THE OPERATING TABLE --AS GOOD AS NEW!

OH TARK!-- I'M SO GLAD YOU'RE WHOLE AGAIN! IT SEEMS LIKE A *MIRACLE*!

SO IT MUST--TO YOU TERRANS, WILMA DEAR! BUT SUCH MIRACLES ARE EVERYDAY TRIVIA TO OUR LORD AND MASTER, OMINU!

LATER... 'WILMA DEAR,' HUH?... ARE YOU SURE YOU NEVER GAVE TARK ANY ENCOURAGEMENT TO MAKE A PASS?

I SUPPOSE I DID TRY USING MY FEMININITY TO WIN OVER TARK!

SEEMS TO HAVE WORKED ABOUT AS WELL AS MY FIRE ALARM PLOY!

IT'S OBVIOUS NOW-- THE ONLY ONE TO DEAL WITH IS OMINU HIMSELF!

LATER...

ARE THEY NOT AMAZING-- THESE NEW LIFE FORMS THAT OUR MASTER HAS CREATED?

VERY!...BUT DON'T YOU FIND IT RATHER LONESOME AND BORING--LIVING IN YOUR SELF- CONTAINED LITTLE WORLD, OMINU?

INDEED! THAT IS WHY I'VE DECIDED TO PLANT A NEW RACE ON YOUR OWN PLANET EARTH!

BUCK ROGERS IN THE 25TH CENTURY

BUCK HAS JUST HAD AN IDEA TO CUT OMINU DOWN TO SIZE!...HE WHISPERS TO COLONEL DEERING---

WE BOTH KNOW OMINU'S *VOICE* IS JUST COMING OVER A LOUDSPEAKER, WILMA! SO HIS VISUAL INPUT MUST BE ELECTRONIC, TOO!

IS SOMETHING DISTURBING YOU, CAPTAIN ROGERS? PERHAPS IT IS THE NEWS THAT I PLAN TO MAKE EARTH *UNLIVABLE* FOR HUMANS -- IN ORDER TO PLANT *MY OWN RACE* THERE!

YEAH, YOU MIGHT SAY I FIND THAT THOUGHT A LITTLE DISTURBING! AND I'M NOT TOO CRAZY ABOUT BEING *SPIED ON* BY YOUR WALL MASKS ALL THE TIME, EITHER!

BY 'WALL MASKS,' OF COURSE, YOU MEAN MY *OMNI-PRESENCE* AND MY *ALL-SEEING EYES*! BUT NO MATTER -- WHAT DO YOU INTEND TO DO, CAPTAIN?

LAWRENCE + MORROW 7-20

IT JUST OCCURRED TO ME -- THERE'S A WAY OF *PULLING DOWN THE SHADES*, SO TO SPEAK -- BY *SHOOTING OUT* YOUR TELE-SCAN MONITORS!

PUBLISHERS CENTRAL BUREAU

1. IF THE PACKAGE DOES NOT CONTAIN ALL TH
IN SEPARATE PARCELS (BECAUSE OF WEIGHT)
2. AN "X" IN THE GREEN COLUMN MEANS
REACHED US AND WILL BE SHIPPED WHEN A
A "✓" IN THE GREEN COLUMN MEANS T
WILL BE SHIPPED WHEN AVAILABLE. OUR LATES
WISH, SUBSTITUTE ITEMS OF INTEREST. OUR N
CREDIT CARD CUSTOMERS: CREDIT WIL
NOT SHIPPED. A NEW CHARGE FOR YOUR B
PAYMENT-WITH-ORDER CUSTOMERS:
AVAILABLE. IF YOU PREFER A REFUND AT ANY TI
WITH YOUR PACKING SLIP TO THE ATT
3. AN "X" IN THE RED COLUMN MEANS WE C
BROCHURE OR CATALOG IS ENCLOSED FRO
CATALOG WILL BE SENT TO YOU SOON FOR
PAYMENT-WITH-ORDER CUSTOMERS:
PREFER A REFUND, PLEASE LET US KNOW ADDR
CREDIT VOUCHER TO THE ATTENTION
4. IF YOU'VE MADE AN OVERPAYMENT TO AVOI
RIGHT), PLEASE SEE NOTE 3 ABOVE
5. SHOULD IT BE NECESSARY TO WRITE, PLEASE
ENCLOSE AN EXPLANATORY LETTER A

91 35 06 25

ER	UNIT PRICE
84	12.95

S CENTRAL BUREAU
ACKING SLIP

PLEASE TEAR HERE ↑

INVOICE

ORDER NO. 11029191

GORDON MORISON

THANK YOU FOR YOU

VALUE	12.95
HDLG	2.25
TOTAL	15.20
RECEIPT	15.20

PAID IN FULL*************

P7 10/28

EXPLANATION OF • CR - AMOUNT DUE YOU
ADJUSTMENT CODE • DR - AMOUNT DUE PCB
FOR GENERAL INFORMATION PLEASE READ THE REVERSE SIDE.

1 CHAMPION AVENUE   AVENEL, N.J. 07001

ITEMS MARKED AS "PICKED." THIS INDICATES THAT THE ITEMS WERE PACKED

SIZE OR POSTAL REGULATIONS) AND SHOULD REACH YOU SHORTLY.

THAT THE ITEM WAS TEMPORARILY OUT OF STOCK WHEN YOUR ORDER

THAT THE ITEM RAN OUT OF STOCK JUST AS YOUR ORDER WAS PICKED AND AVAILABLE.

BROCHURE OR CATALOG IS ENCLOSED FROM WHICH YOU MAY, IF YOU EXT CATALOG WILL BE SENT TO YOU SOON FOR FURTHER ITEM SELECTION.

BE ISSUED AT ONCE FOR THE CHECKED (✓) ITEM THAT WAS CHARGED BUT ACKORDER WILL BE MADE WHEN SHIPPED.

WHILE WE WILL HOLD YOUR ORDER INDEFINITELY AND SHIP WHEN E, PLEASE LET US KNOW ADDRESSING YOUR REQUEST TOGETHER ENTION OF DEPARTMENT REF. AND IT WILL BE PROCESSED PROMPTLY.

AN NO LONGER SUPPLY OR CANNOT RECOGNIZE THE ITEM. OUR LATEST M WHICH YOU MAY FIND SUBSTITUTE ITEMS OF INTEREST. OUR NEXT FURTHER ITEM SELECTION.

TO THE RIGHT IS A CREDIT VOUCHER FOR THE AMOUNT DUE YOU. IF YOU PESSING YOUR REQUEST TOGETHER WITH YOUR ENDORSED N OF DEPARTMENT REF. AND IT WILL BE PROCESSED PROMPTLY.

D DELAYING YOUR ORDER WE'VE PREPARED A CREDIT VOUCHER (TO THE

ENCLOSE THIS PACKING SLIP. IF YOU MAKE A RETURN, PLEASE

ND THIS PACKING SLIP.

BUCK TAKES WHAT HE THINKS IS THE ONE SURE WAY TO SABOTAGE OMINU'S *ALL-SEEING EYE* SYSTEM FOR SPYING ON EVERYTHING THAT HAPPENS ABOARD HIS SPACECRAFT!

FORGIVE MY AMUSEMENT, CAPTAIN! BUT REALLY-- WHAT DO YOU HOPE TO ACCOMPLISH WITH SUCH *FUTILE* LITTLE PLOYS?

THAT'S RIGHT! BEST PUT YOUR GUN AWAY, MY CHILD!

HE CAN STILL SEE EXACTLY WHAT WE'RE DOING!

OF COURSE! DID I NOT TELL YOU OUR LORD AND MASTER IS *OMNISCIENT* AND *ALL-POWERFUL!*

IT'S POSITIVELY *EERIE* HOW OMINU SAW YOU HOLSTERING YOUR RAY-GUN-- EVEN THOUGH YOU'D JUST *SHOT OUT* HIS MASK'S EYES!

COME TO THINK OF IT, THOUGH, WILMA --THOSE WEREN'T THE *ONLY* EYES PRESENT BESIDES OUR OWN!

MEANING WHAT?

TARK WALKED IN JUST THEN-- REMEMBER? AND TARK'S A ROBOT ANDROID-- ONE OF OMINU'S *CREATIONS!*

---JUST LIKE THESE SYNTHETIC ANIMALS!

LAWRENCE & MORROW 7-22

DON'T YOU SEE? THERE MUST BE A *CYBERNETIC* LINKAGE BETWEEN OMINU AND HIS ANDROIDS!

THEY'RE *SLAVED* TO HIM ELECTRONICALLY-- TO FUNCTION AS HIS EYES AND EARS AND HANDS!

IN OTHERWORDS --THEY'RE *SERVO-MECHANISMS* --WHICH ENABLES OMINU TO RUN THE SHIP BY REMOTE CONTROL?

RUN THE SHIP-- AND DEAL WITH US!

OKAY, THAT MAKES SENSE --BUT SO WHAT?

SO MAYBE THERE'S ANOTHER WAY TO BLANK OUT HIS "EYE-SPY" SYSTEM --AND ZERO IN ON THE BOSS-MAN HIMSELF!

LAWRENCE & MORROW 7-23

BUCK ROGERS IN THE 25TH CENTURY ®

IT'S VERY KIND OF YOU, BODON, TO GIVE US THIS PERSONAL TOUR OF YOUR OBSERVATORY!

MY PLEASURE, COLONEL DEERING!

IF BUCK CAN'T DISRUPT OMINU'S "EYE SPY" SYSTEM BY SHOOTING UP THOSE WALL MASKS --MAYBE HE CAN DO SO THROUGH OMINU'S TELE-ROBOTS...SUCH AS BODON, THE SPACECRAFT ASTRONOMER...

YOU SAY, TURNING THIS SWITCH ENABLES YOU TO VIEW OUR SUN *DIRECTLY?*

RIGHT CAPTAIN ROGERS! IT ACTIVATES CERTAIN FILTERS---

WITH THE SWITCH *ON*-- I CAN SCRUTINIZE EVERY ASPECT OF THE SUN--AND INFORM OUR MASTER AT ONCE HOW IT IS REACTING TO HIS MANIPULATIONS!

-- WHICH SCREEN OUT THE DEADLY *SOLAR RAYS* THAT WOULD OTHERWISE BE *TOO INTENSE* TO BEAR!

AIIIIYYEEEBEE!

BUT IF I SHOULD TURN IT *OFF* ---

BUCK ROGERS® IN THE 25TH CENTURY

THE INTENSE FLASH OF SOLAR RADIATION -- ABSORBED BY THE ANDROID ASTRONOMER -- HAS BEEN *TRANSMITTED* INSTANTLY TO HIS MASTER, OMINU -- WITH *TRAUMATIC EFFECTS!*

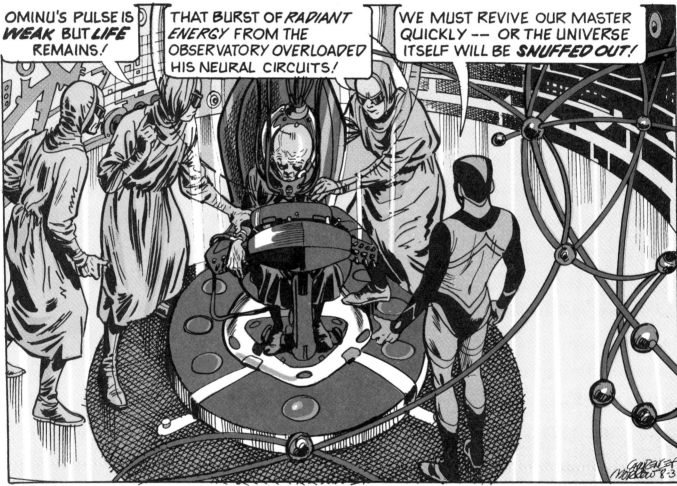

OMINU'S PULSE IS *WEAK* BUT *LIFE* REMAINS!

THAT BURST OF *RADIANT ENERGY* FROM THE OBSERVATORY OVERLOADED HIS NEURAL CIRCUITS!

WE MUST REVIVE OUR MASTER QUICKLY -- OR THE UNIVERSE ITSELF WILL BE *SNUFFED OUT!*

OKAY, WE'VE FOUND THE BOSS-MAN!

AND ALL THAT INSTRUMENT-ATION MUST CONTROL OR MONITOR WHATEVER HE'S DOING TO OUR *SUN!*

I'LL KEEP AN EYE ON THE ANDROIDS, BUCK!

DO THAT, COLONEL! AND I'LL ATTEND TO HIS SOLAR BAG OF TRICKS!

KILLING US WON'T HELP YOUR LORD AND MASTER! LOOK AT HIM --!

WILMA'S CRY BRINGS OMINU'S "CHILDREN" TO SUDDEN, WIDE-EYED ATTENTION-- JUST AS THEY'RE ABOUT TO VENT THEIR DEADLY FURY ON THE TWO EARTHLINGS!

YOUR MEDICAL TECHNOLOGY CAN'T SAVE HIM! ALL IT KNOWS IS HOW TO REPAIR *ARTIFICIAL* CREATURES-- ROBOT ANDROIDS LIKE YOURSELVES!

BUT OMINU'S A *NATURAL ORGANISM*, LIKE CAPTAIN ROGERS AND ME-- BORN FROM A LONG CHAIN OF LIVING CREATURES!

HE NEEDS THE KIND OF HELP HE CAN ONLY GET FROM *TERRAN* PHYSICIANS--IN *TERRAN* HOSPITALS!

WOULD YOU HAVE US BELIEVE SUCH PUNY CREATURES AS YOU EARTHLINGS CAN SAVE OUR *CREATOR*--AND OUR *UNIVERSE*?!

ASK HIM YOURSELVES --IF HE CAN SUMMON ENOUGH STRENGTH TO ANSWER ...

THIS MUCH I'LL TELL YOU FOR CERTAIN, TARK--DESTROY US-- AND YOU'LL DESTROY OMINU'S *ONLY HOPE* FOR SURVIVAL!

SPEAK, OH LORD AND MASTER --WE BESEECH YOU!

IS IT *TRUE* WHAT THE TERRAN FEMALE IS SAYING?!

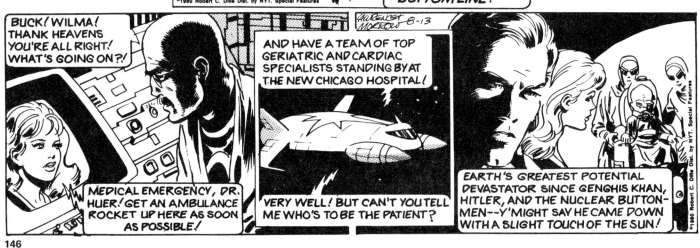

146

AS THE AMBULANCE ROCKET STREAKS EARTHWARD WITH OMINU---

WHAT ARE WE TO DO WITHOUT OUR LORD AND MASTER TO GUIDE US?

FOLLOW HIM DOWN TO EARTH -- NATURALLY! I CAN ASSURE YOU YOU'LL BE RECEIVED AS FRIENDS!

LET US DO AS SHE SAYS! DID NOT OMINU HIMSELF TELL US THE TERRAN FEMALE SPOKE WISELY?

OKAY-- WHAT'S YOUR SECRET THIS TIME?

IN TIMES OF CRISIS, CAPTAIN--A CALM, REASSURING MANNER INSPIRES CONFIDENCE! IT'S CALLED LEADERSHIP!

LOOKS LIKE THE SOLAR PERIL'S OVER, DOC!

QUITE SO! OUR VULCANOLOGISTS AND SEISMOLOGISTS REPORT ALL EARTH INDICATORS STABLE AGAIN!

WHICH REMINDS ME--YOU TWO ARE BEING RECOMMENDED FOR THE MEDAL OF HONOR!

WHAT ABOUT YOURSELF, DR. HUER?

I'M AFRAID I MAY NOT BE AROUND FOR THE CEREMONY! A RATHER EXCITING DEVELOPMENT IS SHAPING UP OUT IN--

CALL FOR DR. HUER! FROM STAR COMMAND RESEARCH!

HUER HERE!

THIS IS BRADBURY AT STAR COMMAND RESEARCH, DOCTOR. WOULD YOU CARE TO TELEPORT OUT TO ARIZONA THIS AFTERNOON?

DON'T TELL ME IT'S READY?!

WE COMPLETED THE FINAL CHECKOUT THIS MORNING!

SAY NO MORE, MY DEAR CHAP! I'M ON MY WAY!

WHAT'S READY?

I'VE NO IDEA!

BUCK ROGERS

IN THE 25TH CENTURY

OMINU'S SPACESHIP HAS BEEN MOVED INTO EARTH-ORBIT ...AND TERRAN ENGINEERS AND SCIENTISTS ARE NOW SWARMING OVER THE CRAFT

THE ANCIENT ALIEN, OMINU HIMSELF--WHO ONCE THREATENED LIFE ON EARTH--HAS BEEN FORCED TO SEEK TERRAN MEDICAL HELP TO PRESERVE HIS OWN FRAIL THREAD OF EXISTENCE!

MEANWHILE, HIS ROBOT-ANDROID "CHILDREN" ARE LEARNING TO FUNCTION AS USEFUL MEMBERS OF A FREE SOCIETY!

BEST OF ALL--EARTH'S GEOLOGIC CRUST IS QUIET, NOW THAT OUR SUN HAS SETTLED DOWN AGAIN INTO A STEADILY GLOWING STAR-- UNDISTURBED BY ARTIFICIALLY TRIGGERED "SOLAR STORMS"!

MEANWHILE, DR. HUER HAS FLOWN TO THE STAR COMMAND RESEARCH CENTER IN THE ARIZONA DESERT TO VIEW HIS LATEST SCIENTIFIC BREAKTHROUGH.

THERE'S ONLY ONE PILOT I'D TRUST TO TEST A SHIP THIS HOT!

GIORDENET MORROWS
8-17

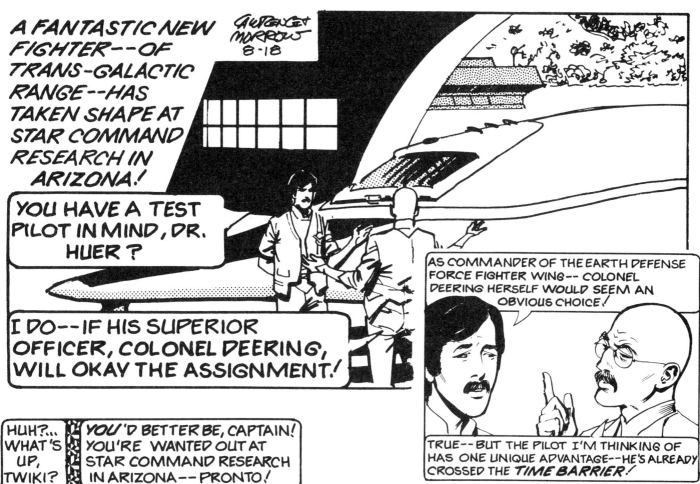

A FANTASTIC NEW FIGHTER--OF TRANS-GALACTIC RANGE--HAS TAKEN SHAPE AT STAR COMMAND RESEARCH IN ARIZONA!

YOU HAVE A TEST PILOT IN MIND, DR. HUER?

I DO--IF HIS SUPERIOR OFFICER, COLONEL DEERING, WILL OKAY THE ASSIGNMENT!

AS COMMANDER OF THE EARTH DEFENSE FORCE FIGHTER WING-- COLONEL DEERING HERSELF WOULD SEEM AN OBVIOUS CHOICE!

TRUE-- BUT THE PILOT I'M THINKING OF HAS ONE UNIQUE ADVANTAGE--HE'S ALREADY CROSSED THE *TIME BARRIER!*

HUH?... WHAT'S UP, TWIKI?

YOU'D BETTER BE, CAPTAIN! YOU'RE WANTED OUT AT STAR COMMAND RESEARCH IN ARIZONA-- PRONTO!

OKAY, OKAY-- SO I'LL HOP THE TWO O'CLOCK ROCKET! WHAT'S ALL THE EXCITEMENT?

ROCKET MY FOOT! I SAID *PRONTO,* BUCKY BOY-- AND THAT MEANS TELEPORTATION!

TELEPORTATION?! LISTEN, I'VE GOT A LUNCH DATE WITH WILMA!

DARN RIGHT YOU DO-- OUT IN ARIZONA! SHE GOT TELEPORTED OUT THERE LAST NIGHT!

BUCK'S MOLECULES ARE INSTANTLY REASSEMBLED-- AFTER BEING TRANSMITTED TO STAR COMMAND RESEARCH IN ARIZONA!

HI, BUCK!

GREETINGS, MY BOY!

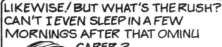

LIKEWISE! BUT WHAT'S THE RUSH? CAN'T I EVEN SLEEP IN A FEW MORNINGS AFTER THAT OMINU CAPER?

YOU WON'T WANT TO-- WHEN YOU SEE WHAT'S ON THE PAD!

JUMPIN' JETS! WHATTA Y'CALL THAT BABY?

TIME STAR-- FOR REASONS WHICH I SHALL EXPLAIN!

ALL STARSHIPS DEVELOP A TIME-WARP CAPABILITY WHEN POWERED BEYOND THE SPEED OF LIGHT!

ELEMENTARY EINSTEIN-IAN PHYSICS, DOCTOR!

QUITE! BUT STAR COMMAND WANTS A FIGHTER THAT CAN STRIKE CLEAR ACROSS THE GALAXY ON SHORT NOTICE

--WHICH REQUIRES A SPEED SO DAZZLING THE MIND CAN CAN SCARCELY CONCIEVE IT!

8/21

TIME STAR HAS THAT SPEED, BUCK--AND THE ONE MAN WHO'S CROSSED THE TIME BARRIER--WE WANT YOU TO PILOT IT!

©1980 Robert C. Dille Dist. by NYT. Special Features

WHAT MADE YOU THINK I'D HAVE TO BE PERSUADED TO FLY THIS SWEETHEART?

YOU DO REALIZE THE DANGERS, BUCK?

SHE'S RIGHT--THEY EXIST! 8/22

THE SPACE-TIME COORDINATES FOR YOUR FLIGHT HAVE BEEN CAREFULLY COMPUTED--BUT JUST BY EXTRAPOLATION!

ERRORS CAN ONLY BE FOUND BY ACTUAL TEST-- MEANING YOU COULD BE HURLED CLEAR OUT OF OUR SPACE-TIME CONTINUUM!

SOMETHING LIKE THAT HAPPENED ONCE AND I SURVIVED--RIGHT? YOU'RE TALKING TO OL' LUCKY BUCK HIMSELF!

THE REVOLUTIONARY TIME STAR TRANS-GALACTIC FIGHTER STREAKS SKYWARD--AT A SPEED WHICH RENDERS IT INVISIBLE TO ANY BUT ELECTRONIC EYES!

BUT NOW HE'S ABOUT TO WITNESS A WEIRD PHENOMENON NO MAN --PERHAPS NO LIVING CREATURE-- HAS EVER EXPERIENCED BEFORE!

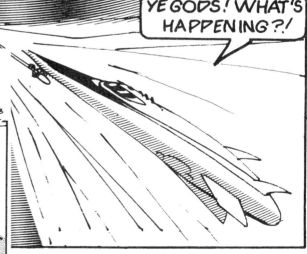

YE GODS! WHAT'S HAPPENING?!

ABOARD IS CAPTAIN BUCK ROGERS --THE ONLY HUMAN EVER TO HAVE CROSSED THE TIME BARRIER-- IN ONE MIND-BOGGLING, FIVE-CENTURY LEAP!

8/23

BUCK ROGERS IN THE 25TH CENTURY

AT STAR COMMAND'S MISSION CONTROL-- COLONEL DEERING AND DR. HUER ARE TENSELY MONITORING THE TEST FLIGHT OF EARTH'S HOTTEST NEW FIGHTER!

WHAT'S WRONG?

SOMETHING'S JAMMING OUR TELEMETERING SIGNALS!

AS *THE* TIME STAR STREAKS ACROSS THE GALAXY--A WEIRD AURA SUDDENLY SUFFUSES THE REVOLUTIONARY CRAFT!

LIKE AN EXPLODING RAINBOW!...JUDAS PRIEST! AM I BLOWING MY MIND.?!

SPACE-TIME COORDINATES TOTALLY ASKEW! THAT *HAS* TO BE THE REASON WE'VE LOST CONTACT.!

I DON'T UNDERSTAND! WASN'T ALL THAT RUN THROUGH THE COMPUTER?!

OF COURSE! BUT THE SHIP'S VELOCITY MUST HAVE EXCEEDED THE TIME WARP CAPACITY OF IT'S ION DRIVE PROPULSION!

WAIT! I'M GETTING A SIGNAL--!

BUCK!...*BUCK!* ...DO YOU READ ME?!

AFFIRMATIVE! *LISTEN!* ANOTHER SHIP'S COMING STRAIGHT AT ME! AND-- *GET THIS!* -- IT'S *EXACTLY LIKE* TIME STAR!

GRAY MORROW 8-24

THE UNIMAGINABLE SPEED OF THE NEW FIGHTER BUCK'S TESTING SEEMS TO BE TRIGGERING EFFECTS UNFORESEEN BY ITS DESIGNER, DR. HUER!

FIRST THAT WEIRD AURA--LIKE THE NORTHERN LIGHTS --AND NOW THIS! AS IF I'M LOOKING AT A *MIRROR IMAGE!*

MIRROR IMAGE?! I-I DON'T UNDERSTAND, BUCK!

NEITHER DO I! ALL I CAN TELL YOU IS--THERE'S A SHIP COMING RIGHT AT ME THAT LOOKS LIKE A *DUPLICATE* OF TIME STAR!

BUCK'S CHANGING COURSE --!

WAIT! NOT YET--!

AT SUCH SPEEDS, HIS SPACE-TIME COORDINATES MUST BE CHECKED FOR EVERY MANEUVER! IT'S *VITAL* FOR HIS OWN SAFETY!

DID YOU HEAR THAT, BUCK ?!

I HEARD--BUT THERE'S NO TIME! EITHER I CHANGE COURSE *NOW*--OR THAT CLONE-SHIP'LL BE UP MY NOSE!

WHAT HAPPENED ?

I'M NOT SURE--THE TRANSMISSION FADED!

TITANIC FORCES *WRENCH* THE HULL OF TIME STAR AS BUCK VEERS TO AVOID COLLISION *WITH HIS CRAFT'S APPARENT CLONE!*

THEY MAY NOT BELIEVE ME BACK AT STAR COMMAND--BUT THEY'LL *HAVE* TO BELIEVE *VIDEO PROOF!*

AS THE CLONE SHIPS VEER AND PASS--BUCK RECORDS THE ENCOUNTER ON HIS VIDEO-SCANNER!

GOTCHA!

NEXT QUESTION-- DID A TERRAN SPY COP THE PLANS FOR *TIME STAR?*--OR WAS THE PILOT AN *ALIEN?!*

LET'S GO TO THE VIDEO-TAPE--!

YOU'VE LOST CONTACT?

MAYBE NOT!...LIEUTENANT! CAN YOU GET ME MORE GAIN ON THAT SIGNAL?

NO USE! WE'VE LOST HIS SIGNAL!

THE SHIFT IN COURSE DID IT--PROBABLY MAGNIFIED THE TIME-WARP EFFECT!

MEANWHILE, BUCK PLAYS BACK THE VIDEO TAPE OF THE MYSTERIOUS CLONE-CRAFT--

PERFECT SHOT! THERE'S THE PILOT--VISIBLE THROUGH THE TRANSPARENT CANOPY! NOW TO ZOOM IN CLOSER--TO SEE IF HE'S ALIEN OR--

HOLY HOLOGRAMS! HE'S *ME*--!

LAWRENCE + MORROW 8/29

LET ME TRY THOSE RECEIVER CIRCUITS, COLONEL!

THERE'S STILL HOPE OF RE-ESTABLISHING CONTACT ----IF I CAN APPROXIMATE BUCK'S TIME-SPACE COORDINATES!

WHILE FAR ACROSS THE GALAXY--

STEADY ON, PAL! THE VIDEO-SCREEN CAN'T LIE!

TROUBLE IS, IT CAN'T TALK, EITHER! SO HOW CAN I BE IN *TWO DIFFERENT SHIPS* AT THE *SAME INSTANT?!*

BUCK ROGERS IN THE 25TH CENTURY®

UNBEARABLE TENSION MOUNTS AT STAR COMMAND'S MISSION CONTROL!... ALL CONTACT HAS BEEN LOST WITH CAPTAIN ROGERS IN THE NEW TRANS-GALACTIC FIGHTER, TIME STAR!

NO VOICE COMMUNICATION --NO FURTHER TELEMETERING TRANSMISSION! WE'D BETTER FACE IT... BUCK'S GONE!

ARE YOU TELLING US THE TIME STAR JUST... JUST **BLEW UP**?!

AN EERIE RADIO SILENCE HAS FALLEN ABOARD TIME STAR--AS BUCK RACES ACROSS THE GALAXY AT MIND-BOGGLING SPEED!

NOW HEAR THIS, DOC-- WILMA! I GOT A VIDEO-FREEZE ON THE PILOT OF THAT SHIP THAT PASSED!

HE LOOKED **EXACTLY LIKE ME!**--HE COULD'VE BEEN MY **IDENTICAL TWIN!**

HEY, DID YOU GET THAT?... CALLING STAR COMMAND! ...BLAST IT ALL, **DO YOU READ ME**?!

NOTHING! NOT A WORD! AND NO RECEPTION ON THE OTHER BANDS!

NEVER MIND--COOL IT, PAL! MAYBE THEY'RE RECEIVING ME--EVEN IF I CAN'T READ **THEM!**

I'LL KNOW AS SOON AS I CONTACT THE PYLON OBSERVERS! TIME STAR CALLING PYLON!

WHILE AT STAR COMMAND'S OUTPOST ON THE PYLON PLANETOID--MARKING THE OTHER END OF THE TEST-FLIGHT COURSE---

ANY SIGNAL FROM TIME STAR?... WE SHOULD HAVE IT ON RADAR BY NOW!

NEGATIVE, SIR! NO S-T COORDINATES--NO TELEMETRY--NO WORD FROM THE PILOT!

BUCK HAS SEEN HIMSELF FLYING IN THE OPPOSITE DIRECTION IN ANOTHER TIME STAR! AND NOW AS HE NEARS THE END OF HIS ZOOM ACROSS THE GALAXY---

REPEAT! TIME STAR CALLING PYLON!... DO YOU READ ME?!

STILL NO ANSWER! SOMETHING'S GOTTA BE WRONG WITH MY TRANSMISSION!... NEVER MIND--THEY'LL HAVE ME ON RADAR SOON!

BUT MINUTES LATER ON THE PYLON PLANETOID MARKING THE END OF THE COURSE---

HE'S DEFINATELY OVERDUE, SIR-- UNLESS THIS TRAJECTORY TIME-PLOT'S ALL WRONG!

PYLON PLANETOID DEAD AHEAD!...PRAISE BE! AT LEAST THERE'S NOTHING WRONG WITH MY ASTRO-GUIDANCE SYSTEM!

BUT WHAT IN BLAZES HAPPENED TO THEIR SIGNAL BEACON?... IT'S SUPPOSED TO CHANGE COLOR ON RADAR ECHO!

WHILE AT THE OBSERVATION POST ON THE PYLON PLANETOID---

BETTER NOTIFY STAR COMMAND-- NOTHING YET ON OUR SCANNERS!

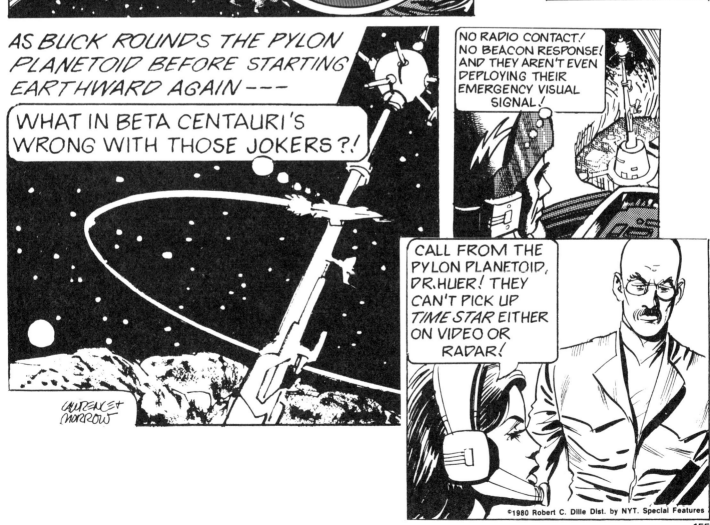

AS BUCK ROUNDS THE PYLON PLANETOID BEFORE STARTING EARTHWARD AGAIN---

WHAT IN BETA CENTAURI'S WRONG WITH THOSE JOKERS?!

NO RADIO CONTACT! NO BEACON RESPONSE! AND THEY AREN'T EVEN DEPLOYING THEIR EMERGENCY VISUAL SIGNAL!

CALL FROM THE PYLON PLANETOID, DR. HUER! THEY CAN'T PICK UP TIME STAR EITHER ON VIDEO OR RADAR!

156

BUCK ROGERS® IN THE 25TH CENTURY

BUCK'S *WEIRD ISOLATION* CONTINUES AS HE BLASTS THROUGH SPACE IN THAT UNCHARTED SPEED ZONE KNOWN ONLY AS THE *ULTRA TIME WARP!*

FACE IT, PAL--SOMETHING *HAS* TO BE WRONG! WHY ELSE WOULD THE PYLON OBSERVERS IGNORE YOUR MANEUVER?!

WHILE TIME STAR HURTLES EARTHWARD -- A TERRAN SURVIVOR OF A SPACE SHIPWRECK IS COMING TO ABOARD A STRANGE CRAFT---

YOUR SHIP EXPLODED?

IT MUST'VE! I REMEMBER A GAS CLOUD FOGGING US IN-- THEN A BLAST-- AND NEXT THING I WAKE UP HERE!

YOU WERE ADRIFT WITH NO UMBILICAL CORD WHEN I PICKED YOU UP!

THANKS FOR SAVING ME! ANY HOPE OF GETTING A LIFT BACK TO MY OWN PLANET?

I FEAR NOT! I AM STATIONED *HERE* ON SENTRY DUTY-- WHILE MY RULER MARSHALS HIS FORCES FOR WAR!

WAR?! ...WHAT WAR? AND WHAT FORCES?!

THOSE YOU SEE THROUGH THE PILOT WINDOW!

LEAPIN' LASERS! THE *DRACONIAN BATTLE FLEET!*

THE SALLY O'S SPACE WRECKED SKIPPER REVIVES FROM THE MYSTERY GAS TO FIND HIMSELF ABOARD A DRACONIAN SENTRY CRAFT -- ON *WAR DUTY!*

WOW! THERE'S ENOUGH FIRE POWER OUT THERE TO BLAST ANY PLANET RIGHT OUT OF ORBIT!

HOWEVER--SINCE YOU WERE HELPLESSLY ADRIFT IN SPACE WHEN I PICKED YOU UP--*YOU* SURELY CANNOT ENDANGER HIS PLANS!

CORRECT! I WAS POSTED HERE TO STOP ANY SHIP FROM GETTING CLOSE ENOUGH TO DISCOVER THE EMPEROR'S WAR PLANS!

CORVETTE SENTRY ROBOT GAMMA-139 CALLING FLEET-INTEL! HAVE TAKEN ABOARD CASTAWAY FROM TERRAN MERCHANTMAN!....WILL AWAIT INSTRUCTIONS!

A *TERRAN?!*...YOU SQUAWKING HEAP OF SPACE JUNK! YOU MICRON-HEADED BOOBY! YOU WERE PROGRAMED TO BAR *ALL* INTRUDERS FROM THIS SECTOR!

YOU THINK HIS MAJESTY, THE EMPEROR DRACO, WANTS *ANY* OBSERVER --LEAST OF ALL AN EARTHLING--TO WITNESS OUR PREPARATIONS TO *INVADE* THAT PLANET?!

NO UNAUTHORIZED OBSERVER MUST BE LEFT ALIVE WHO COULD REPORT THE MARSHALING OF THE DRACONIAN WAR FLEET!

UNDERSTOOD!...THE TERRAN CASTAWAY SHALL BE ATOMIZED AND DISPERSED PROMPTLY VIA ION EXHAUST!

...OH YEAH ?!

158

STARGATE -- THE ONLY SAFE ENTRY ROUTE THROUGH EARTH'S FORCE-FIELD DEFENSE MAZE ... AN APPROACHING CRAFT IS HALTED AND CHALLENGED BY A TERRAN FIGHTER!

IDENTIFY YOURSELF!

TERRAN PILOT -- IN A HIJACKED DRACONIAN CORVETTE!

A VIDEO FLASH ALERTS COLONEL DEERING OF THE EARTH DEFENSE FIGHTER WING TO A SUSPICIOUS INTRUDER -- ALLEGEDLY BRINGING **URGENT SECRET NEWS!**

THE HIJACKER SAYS HE'S ARTHUR CLARKE -- MASTER OF THE SPACE TRAMP, SALLY O -- EARTH TO CASSIOPEIA RUN!

SKIPPER AND SHIP CHECK OUT, COLONEL! SPECTROSCOPIC SCAN SHOWS HIJACKED CRAFT TO BE MADE OF DRACONIAN ALLOYS!

GOOD ENOUGH! ... HOLD HIM AT STARGATE, MAJOR!

WILCO!

WHAT'S THE DRILL, COLONEL?

I'LL TAKE MY OWN FIGHTER -- YOU TAKE *STARLAB* AND SCREEN HIM FROM STEM TO STERN, DOCTOR!

IF HE DOESN'T ADD UP -- I'LL CHECK HIM OUT THE HARD WAY!

LAWRENCE + MORROWS 9/14

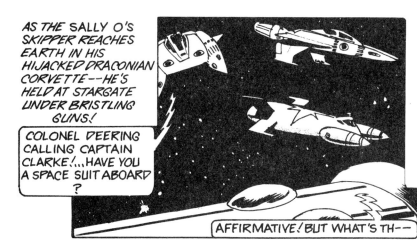

AS THE SALLY O'S SKIPPER REACHES EARTH IN HIS HIJACKED DRACONIAN CORVETTE--HE'S HELD AT STARGATE UNDER BRISTLING GUNS!

COLONEL DEERING CALLING CAPTAIN CLARKE!...HAVE YOU A SPACE SUIT ABOARD?

AFFIRMATIVE! BUT WHAT'S TH--

NEVER MIND THE QUESTIONS! JUST FOLLOW ORDERS!

GET SUITED UP--LEAVE THE CORVETTE--AND JET OVER TO STARLAB! THAT'S THE SHIP ON YOUR PORT BEAM!

WHILE CAPTAIN CLARKE IS CARRYING OUT WILMA'S ORDERS -- SHE CALLS DR. HUER IN STARLAB---

CAN YOUR INSTRUMENTS DETECT ANYONE STILL ABOARD THE CORVETTE, DOCTOR--OR ANY EVIDENCE OF EXPLOSIVE CARGO?

NEGATIVE!

YOU REALIZE, OF COURSE, COLONEL DEERING--THIS IN NO WAY PROVES THE SHIP IS HARMLESS?

UNDERSTOOD, DOCTOR! ...MAJOR THORNE, KEEP ME COVERED WHILE I INSPECT THE SHIP PERSONALLY!

MAJOR THORNE CALLING COLONEL DEERING!

I RESPECTFULLY REQUEST-- CORRECTION! URGENTLY REQUEST-- THAT YOU ALLOW ME TO CHECK OUT THE CORVETTE!

WHEN I WANT YOUR TACTICAL ADVICE, MAJOR --I'LL ASK FOR IT!

...BUT THANKS ANYHOW!

WARILY WILMA BOARDS THE DRACONIAN CORVETTE THROUGH ITS ENTRY HATCH---

NO SIGN OF LIFE --YET! BUT THIS CRATE COULD BE BOOBY-TRAPPED TO THE NINES!

AT THAT SAME MOMENT--TIME STAR IS CARRYING BUCK RIGHT INTO THE MIDST OF THE DRACONIAN BATTLE FLEET!

LAWRENCE + MORROWS 9/18

COLONEL DEERING TO STARLAB AND FIGHTER! THE CORVETTE APPEARS A-O-K!

CLARKE'S STORY ABOUT CLOBBERING THE SENTRY ROBOT CHECKS OUT--AND I FIND NO TRACE OF CONCEALED EXPLOSIVE!

SOMETHING'S GOTTA BE WRONG! DRACONIAN MEN-OF-WAR ALL AROUND ME--AND SO FAR NOT ONE HAS EVEN CHALLENGED ME!

ONE THING'S SURE-- DRACO DIDN'T MASS ALL THESE BATTLE-WAGONS HERE JUST SO HE COULD ADMIRE HIS HARDWARE!

BUT WHAT KINDA CUTE GAME IS HE UP TO--LETTING AN ENEMY SPY LIKE ME SNEAK RIGHT THROUGH HIS WHOLE FLEET ?!

EVEN HIS PICKET CRAFT DIDN'T PICK ME UP ON RADAR!

OKAY PAL -- SO WE'LL WORRY ABOUT THAT LATER! WE'RE NOT HOME SAFE YET!

BUCK ROGERS

IN THE 25TH CENTURY

CAPTAIN CLARKE LANDS IN HIS HIJACKED DRACONIAN CORVETTE UNDER THE PERSONAL ESCORT OF WILMA AND DR. HUER!

WHAT HAPPENS NOW, COLONEL DEERING?

YOU'RE GOING TO TELL THE DEFENSE DIRECTORATE EXACTLY WHAT YOU TOLD US--ABOUT DRACO'S INVASION PLANS!

UNAWARE OF THE SPACE SKIPPER'S REPORT OF AN IMPENDING DRACONIAN ATTACK-- BUCK RETURNS TO EARTH WITH HIS OWN FANTASTIC WAR ALARM!

WHO'S GONNA BELIEVE SUCH A STORY--?!

--THAT I PLOWED RIGHT THROUGH THE WHOLE DRACONIAN BATTLE FLEET WITHOUT BEING STOPPED OR SPOTTED?!

NEVER MIND! IT'S UP TO YOU TO CONVINCE 'EM, PAL!

FIRST THING IS TO GET DOWN TO NEW CHICAGO IN ONE PIECE-- EVEN THOUGH MY RADIO'S DEAD!

SPEAK OF THE DEVIL! HERE'S A FIGHTER ESCORT NOW

BUT HEY! WHAT'S THAT IDIOT DOING--BANKING RIGHT INTO MY PATH?!

YE GODS! CAN'T HE SEE ME?! THERE'S NO WAY TO AVOID HIM!

NO! I DON'T BELIEVE IT! OUR SHIPS ARE PASSING RIGHT THROUGH EACH OTHER--!!

OKAY, PAL--JUST HANG IN THERE LONG ENOUGH TO REPORT THAT DRACONIAN WAR FLEET TO THE DEFENSE BRASS!

THE HARROWING TEST FLIGHT OF *TIME STAR* IS ALMOST OVER... BUT AN EVEN *MORE UNNERVING* EXPERIENCE OCCURS AS BUCK RETURNS TO EARTH!

THAT DOES IT!...I'VE *GOTTA* BE HALLUCINATING!

FIRST I PASS MYSELF COMING BACK--AND NOW A FIGHTER ZOOMS RIGHT *THROUGH* ME!

THEN IT'S EITHER A NICE PEACEFUL STRETCH OF R+R--OR A HEART-TO-HEART CHAT WITH A SHRINK!

STILL NO RESPONSE FROM MISSION CONTROL! AND THERE'S THE DRONE SECURITY CRAFT CIRCLING THE FIELD---

-- WHICH MEANS ALL OPERATIONS HAVE BEEN SHUT DOWN!

DON'T BOTHER TRYING TO FIGURE IT OUT, BUCKY BOY-- JUST BLAST ON TO NEW CHICAGO AND MAKE YOUR REPORT!

CAUGHLE MORROW 9/23

MEANWHILE...

RELAX, MY DEAR!

THERE'S NOTHING WE CAN DO ABOUT THE DRACONIAN THREAT--UNTIL THE DEFENSE DIRECTORATE HEARS CAPTAIN CLARKE'S STORY!

THE DEFENSE DIRECTORATE HAVE ALL ARRIVED--AND WILL MEET IN THE FEDERATION COUNCIL HALL IN TEN MINUTES!

AT LAST!

BUCK HAS JUST LANDED IN TIME STAR--UNDER WEIRD CIRCUMSTANCES!

GREAT! NO ORDERS FROM THE TOWER --NOBODY TALKS ME DOWN-- NO ONE EVEN SEES *TIME STAR* LAND! ...WHAT GOES ON ?!

THANK *GOODNESS!* THERE'S WILMA AND DR. HUER!

HEY, WILMA!

K-2VI

WILMA! DOC! CAN'T YOU SEE ME?... WHAT AM I--A *GHOST*?

THE DIRECTORATE MAY NOT WANT TO FACE THE FACT THAT DRACO PLANS TO INVADE US--BUT THEY'LL *HAVE* TO BELIEVE CAPTAIN CLARKE!

WHILE ABOARD THE EMPEROR'S MIGHTY FLAGSHIP, DRACONIA--

YOUR HIGHNESS'S CHIEF INTELLIGENCE OFFICER--YAR VORK --HAS COME TO REPORT!

SPEAK THEN, YAR VORK! WHAT IS IT YOU WISH TO TELL ME?

THE OUTCOME OF OUR DECOY STRATEGY-- CODE-NAMED: THE *CASTAWAY CAPER!*

THE EMPEROR DRACO'S CHIEF OF INTELLIGENCE HAS COME TO REPORT ON A CUNNING *DECOY STRATEGY--*

AH YES! YOUR SCHEME INVOLVED A TERRAN SPACE CAPTAIN, DID IT NOT?

CORRECT, YOUR MAJESTY! HE WAS TRICKED INTO BELIEVING HIS SHIP HAD BEEN LOST-- DUE TO A MYSTERIOUS GAS CLOUD!

EVENTUALLY, I PRESUME, HE WOULD FIND HIMSELF RESCUED

BY ONE OF OUR ROBOT SENTRY CRAFT-- FROM WHICH HE WOULD *APPARENTLY* WITNESS OUR PREPARATIONS TO INVADE THE EARTH!

WHAT EXACTLY DID THE TERRAN CAPTAIN SEE?

HE THINKS HE SAW THE DRACONIAN WAR FLEET --AND OVERHEARD TALK OF OUR SECRET PLAN TO ATTACK HIS EARTH!

BRILLIANT--IF THE TRICK WORKS! BUT HOW IS HE TO CONVEY THIS *MISINFORMATION* BACK TO EARTH?

NO PROBLEM, YOUR MAJESTY!

THE ROBOT WAS PROGRAMMED TO TURN ITS BACK--WHILE THE EARTHLING REACHED OUT FOR A *BLUNT INSTRUMENT!*

BUCK ROGERS *IN THE 25th CENTURY* ®

COLONEL DEERING AND DR. HUER HAVE CALLED A COUNCIL OF WAR TO PUT THE EARTH FEDERATION ON INSTANT ALERT!

OUR PLANET MAY BE ABOUT TO FACE INVASION!... CAPTAIN CLARKE HERE WILL TELL YOU WHY!

WHILE EARTH'S DEFENSE DIRECTORATE HEARS THE TRAMP SKIPPER'S ALARMING NEWS -- EMPEROR DRACO IS ALSO GETTING A REPORT---

SO YOU FOOLED THE TERRAN CAPTAIN?

COMPLETELY, YOUR HIGHNESS!

©1980 Robert C. Dille Dist. by NYT. Special Features

THE SO-CALLED 'SPACE CLOUD' WHICH GASSED HIS CREW -- AND LEFT HIM A CASTAWAY -- WAS *NERVE DUST-17* SPREAD BY DRACONIAN GHOST CRAFT!

AND THE WAR FLEET WHICH HE WILL SWEAR HE SAW MARSHALING TO ATTACK EARTH --?

A MERE LASER-HOLOGRAM, PROJECTED FROM THE NOSE OF THE CRAFT THAT PICKED HIM UP!

HOW CLEVER OF YOU, YAR VORK! ... SO NOW WHEN THE TERRANS RUSH TO FEND OFF THIS IMAGINARY BLOW--

THEY WILL LEAVE STARGATE WIDE OPEN FOR YOUR SUBLIME MAJESTY'S *REAL* ATTACK!

CAPTAIN CLARKE'S STORY ABOUT HIS OWN SHIP-- AND HIJACKING THE DRACONIAN SENTRY CRAFT-- CHECKS OUT IN EVERY TECHNICAL DETAIL!

OUR MOST RIGOROUS PSYCHO-EMOTIONAL AND MIND-SCANNING TESTS *CONFIRM* THAT HE'S TELLING THE *TRUTH*

HOLD IT, BUCKY BOY! IF CLARKE'S NOT A LIAR-- WHAT DOES THAT MAKE *ME* ?

©1980 Robert C. Dille Dist. by NYT. Special Features

WE CAN'T *BOTH* HAVE SEEN THE DRACONIAN WAR FLEET IN *OPPOSITE* DIRECTIONS FROM THE EARTH...UNLESS ...

WAIT A MINUTE --!

-- WHEN I PUSHED TIME STAR PAST *LIGHT SPEED* I MUST'VE WARPED INTO ANOTHER DIMENSION! MY MOLECULES ARE NOW MOVING AT AN ACCELERATED RATE-THUS MAKING ME INAUDIBLE AND INVISIBLE TO MY COMPATRIOTS....

10-1
GURELEY + MORROW

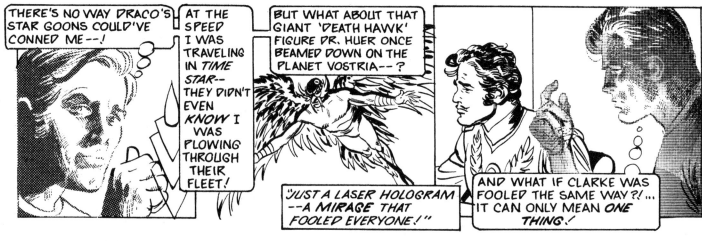

THERE'S NO WAY DRACO'S STAR GOONS COULD'VE CONNED ME--!

AT THE SPEED I WAS TRAVELING IN *TIME STAR*-- THEY DIDN'T EVEN *KNOW* I WAS PLOWING THROUGH THEIR FLEET!

BUT WHAT ABOUT THAT GIANT 'DEATH HAWK' FIGURE DR. HUER ONCE BEAMED DOWN ON THE PLANET VOSTRIA--?

"JUST A LASER HOLOGRAM --A *MIRAGE* THAT FOOLED EVERYONE!"

AND WHAT IF CLARKE WAS FOOLED THE SAME WAY?!... IT CAN ONLY MEAN *ONE THING!*

VERY WELL THEN-- IF WE ACCEPT CAPTAIN CLARKE'S REPORT-- WHAT EXACTLY ARE YOU PROPOSING, COLONEL?

THAT WE FORCE DRACO'S HAND-- BY CONFRONTING HIM AND MAKING HIM FIGHT NOW--*BEFORE* HE CAN INVADE OUR PLANET!

THE ODDS WILL STILL BE HEAVILY AGAINST US-- BUT AT LEAST THE ELEMENT OF SURPRISE WILL BE *OURS!*

NO--*NO!* CAN'T YOU SEE YOU'LL JUST BE PLAYING DRACO'S GAME?--LEAVING STARGATE UNDEFENDED FOR HIM TO *SNEAK RIGHT IN!*

FOR PETE'S SAKE-- CAN'T *ANYONE* HEAR ME?!

WHAT ABOUT OUR ELECTROMAGNETIC SHIELD-- OUR TERRAN FORCE-FIELD MAZE?

YOU THINK THAT CAN'T BE BLOWN APART WITH A HEAVY ENOUGH LASER AND PARTICLE-BEAM BARRAGE?

QUESTION-- HOW CAN I BLOW OPEN THEIR ⑥★!! *DEAF EARS* ?!

ERR-FZZT!... VLOP-BEEP!

TROUBLE, SACCO* ?

LAWRENCE + MORROW 10/4

SOME *ODD* FORM OF RADION MUST BE PRESENT!/... I CAN FEEL IT AFFECTING MY MAGNETIC INDUCTANCE!

©1980 Robert C. Dille Dist. by NYT. Special Features

SUPREME ADVISORY COMPUTER

COLONEL DEERING CONDUCTS A HASTY BRIEFING BEFORE TAKEOFF!

I'LL LEAD THE FIRST ASSAULT --UNLESS DRACO'S FORCE SIGNALS ANY WILLINGNESS TO PARLEY!

WHICH COULD WELL BE SUSPICIOUS IN ITSELF!...MY INSTRUMENTATION IN *STARLAB* WILL BE ATTUNED TO DETECT ANY TREACHERY!

C'MON! TRY DETECTING *ME!*

WHILE--

ANY SIGN THE TERRANS HAVE TAKEN OUR BAIT?

OUR SCANNERS ARE SWEEPING EARTH, YOUR MAJESTY! THE MOMENT THEIR FORCE IS LAUNCHED, WE SHALL MOVE ON STARGATE!

I MUST BE SEEING THINGS!

WHAT DO YOU MEAN, DR. HUER?

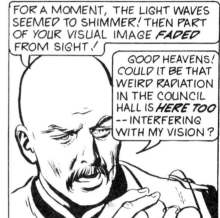

FOR A MOMENT, THE LIGHT WAVES SEEMED TO SHIMMER! THEN PART OF YOUR VISUAL IMAGE *FADED* FROM SIGHT!

GOOD HEAVENS! COULD IT BE THAT WEIRD RADIATION IN THE COUNCIL HALL IS *HERE TOO* --INTERFERING WITH MY VISION?

NO-- *WAIT!* I NOTICE IT TOO!

WHICH ALMOST SEEMS TO INDICATE--HMM!

INDICATE *WHAT,* DR. HUER?

IT'S AS IF SOMETHING IS IN BETWEEN US-- PREVENTING US FROM SEEING EACH OTHER COMPLETELY!

EXACTLY THE WAY *I* PERCEIVE IT, WILMA!

THAT THE RADIATION --OR INTERFERENCE-- MAY INDEED BE CONCENTRATED IN THE FORM OF SOME *ALIEN PRESENCE!*

BUT ANY SUCH EXPLANATION IS REALLY TOO FANTASTIC TO BE TAKEN SERIOUSLY!

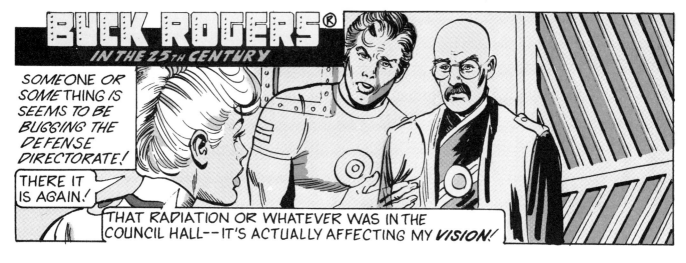

CONVINCED THE DRACONIANS ARE MASSING IN SECTOR SIGMA-17-NORTH, WILMA LEADS A STRIKE FORCE TO HALT THE INVASION!

LET'S JUST PRAY THAT *INTERFERENCE PHENOMENON* DOESN'T AFFECT OUR TACTICAL COMPUTERS!

WHILE ABOARD THE EMPEROR DRACO'S FLAGSHIP IN A TOTALLY DIFFERENT SECTOR OF SPACE---

THE TERRAN FORCE HAS TAKEN OFF, YOUR MAJESTY-- HEADING FOR SIGMA-17-NORTH!

SPLENDID! THEN PROCEED WITH THE *ATTACK ON STARGATE!*

WITH THE TERRAN FLEET DECOYED TO THE WRONG SECTOR--BUCK MUST COPE ALONE WITH THE ENTIRE ENEMY FORCE!

ONE SECRET WEAPON --IF IT WORKS!

MY SPATIO-TEMPORAL VIBES DEFINITELY RATTLED THE DEFENSE DIRECTORATE! MAYBE THEY CAN DO THE SAME FOR DRACO'S STAR GOONS!

TROUBLE, ADMIRAL?

SOMETHING IS AFFECTING OUR INSTRUMENTATION!

WHAT ARE YOU IMPLYING, ADMIRAL? AN OUTBURST OF COSMIC RADIATION?

I'VE NO IDEA *WHAT'S* CAUSING THE TROUBLE!

EITHER OUR STARSHIP CAPTAINS ARE HAVING NERVOUS BREAKDOWNS -- OR OUR GUIDANCE SYSTEMS HAVE GONE CRAZY!

AS BUCK'S ULTRA-TIME-WARP FIGHTER SPREADS A BEWILDERING WAKE OF VIBRATIONS THROUGH THE DRACONIAN WAR FLEET---

ANOTHER COLLISION!

SCRATCH NINE!

THE ATTACK HAS BEEN HALTED, SIRE! WHAT ARE YOUR MAJESTY'S ORDERS?

NEED YOU ASK, FOOL?! IT IS *WE* WHO WERE DECOYED TO DISASTER-- NOT THE TERRANS!

MEANWHILE--BUCK'S JUBILATION IS STRANGELY SHORT-LIVED!

OKAY, GREAT! SO WE'VE PULLED OFF THE WORST DRACONIAN DEFEAT IN RECENT GALACTIC HISTORY--!

BUT WHAT'S HAPPENING TO YOUR HEAD, PAL? SUDDENLY I'M *SEEING DOUBLE!*

AS *THE DRACONIAN FLEET WITHDRAWS IN PANIC FROM ITS ATTACK ON EARTH--TIME STAR BEGINS TO GIVE OFF A WEIRD RAINBOW AURA!*

WHERE HAVE I SEEN *THAT* BEFORE--?!

INSIDE THE REVOLUTIONARY TRANS-GALACTIC FIGHTER CRAFT ---

SAME PHENOMENON AS WHEN I CRASHED THROUGH THE ULTRA-TIME-WARP BARRIER ON MY TEST FLIGHT!

WHICH CAN ONLY MEAN *ONE THING*--!

THOSE EXPLOSIONS--AND THE RADIATION FALLOUT--WHEN THOSE DRACONIAN WARSHIPS CRASHED INTO OUR DEFENSIVE FORCE-FIELD--!

THEY MUST HAVE JARRED ME *BACK*--THROUGH THE ULTRA-TIME-WARP BARRIER!

AS THE TERRAN STRIKE FORCE ZOOMS EARTHWARD---

THAT WEIRD GLOW UP AHEAD! WHAT IS IT, DR. HUER? DID THE ENEMY GET THROUGH STARGATE?!

WE'LL SOON KNOW, WILMA!

177

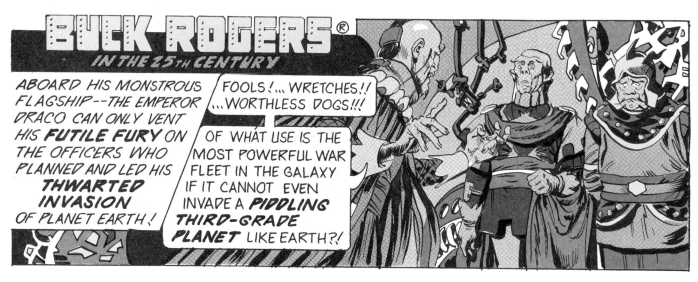

BUCK ROGERS ®
IN THE 25TH CENTURY

ABOARD HIS MONSTROUS FLAGSHIP--THE EMPEROR DRACO CAN ONLY VENT HIS **FUTILE FURY** ON THE OFFICERS WHO PLANNED AND LED HIS **THWARTED INVASION** OF PLANET EARTH!

FOOLS!... WRETCHES!! ...WORTHLESS DOGS!!!

OF WHAT USE IS THE MOST POWERFUL WAR FLEET IN THE GALAXY IF IT CANNOT EVEN INVADE A **PIDDLING THIRD-GRADE PLANET** LIKE EARTH?!

AS THE TERRAN DEFENDERS RETURN TO EARTH--THEY FIND THAT THE EXPLOSION OF THE DRACONIAN WARSHIPS HAS JARRED BUCK AND HIS REVOLUTIONARY FIGHTER CRAFT BACK INTO HIS OWN NORMAL TIME-SPACE CONTINUUM!

DR. HUER! LOOK! AND TELL ME I'M NOT DREAMING!...THAT **IS** TIME STAR, ISN'T IT ?!

AFFIRMATIVE, WILMA! I SEE IT, TOO!

10/26 LAWRENCE & MORROW   ©1980 Robert C. Dille Dist. by NYT. Special Features

AND IF THAT'S TIME STAR, THEN **BUCK** MUST BE ABOARD!

YOU WERE EXPECTING, MAYBE, THE LONE RANGER?